# How to HACCP 3rd Ed...

## A Management Guid...

# FOREWORD

Hazard Analysis Critical Control Point (HACCP) has become increasingly important for all food businesses as an effective means of ensurin... ...lation.
HAC(... ...ctions
of foc... ...ervice.
Adopt... ...elp to
facilit... ...o your
custor...

Curre... ...ACCP
and th... ...actical
guide... ...ype of
book... ...third
edition... ...nse to
reader... ...meets
new tr... ...small
and m... ...cessful
and ef...

The a... ...of the
World... ...n and
the Na... ...ria for
Foods...

The au... ...d and
has m... ...ACCP
develo... ...is the
Head... ...Wales
Institu... ...points
within... ...ith a
multidi... ...prove
food h...

# How to HACCP 3rd Edition

## Contents

# How to HACCP 3rd Edition

## Contents Continued

## Stage 0 Knowing the Basics.

### 0.1. - Introduction and Reason for the Book.

This section is designed to answer the following questions, frequently asked by food businesses and their employees.

**WHAT IS HACCP?**

**WHY DO WE NEED IT?**

**HOW CAN WE LEARN ABOUT HACCP?**

Hazard Analysis Critical Control Point (HACCP) is a food safety management system, which concentrates prevention strategies on known hazards and the risks of them occurring at specific points in the food chain.

HACCP works in conjunction with pre-requisite practices (PRPs). This is an umbrella term used to describe all those activities, other than specific HACCP plans, which affect food safety. PRPs form the foundations upon which HACCP is built. This book is primarily concerned with HACCP but PRPs are critical to food safety.

PRPs + HACCP = Safe Food

PRPs — General activities influencing food safety: good hygiene practices/good manufacturing practices. Includes pest control, cleaning, training.

HACCP — Food safety management system based upon hazards and validated control measures operated at critical control points.

It is this specificity which makes HACCP so effective and the approach easily integrates into Total Quality Management or ISO 9000. Developing HACCP assists companies to comply with legislation, supports due diligence and fulfils customer requirements for a food and safety management system. The introduction of a common food hygiene approach across the European Community through Directive 93/43/EEC was achieved within the UK in 1995 by the Food Safety (General Food Hygiene) Regulations which legally require the HACCP approach. Industry guides to good hygienic practice are voluntary guides providing more detailed advice on complying with the regulations as they relate to specific sectors.

Food safety should be given the highest priority, however companies are often short of time and appropriate personnel require training, especially in food safety, which needs to be widely disseminated throughout their company. Food safety management systems are much more likely to be effective if they are owned by all in production and management.

Traditional HACCP training can be expensive and may lack practical information on how to design and implement HACCP. This book comes at a time when the demands to learn about HACCP have never been greater.

The aim of this book is to to assist companies in the practical development of a HACCP system by clearly explaining the methods or information required to complete each HACCP stage. Small businesses that lack the resources of larger companies, environmental health officers, as well as students will find the simple explanations of the methods used in the development of HACCP systems particularly useful. Unlike other books, the amount of text has been kept to a minimum and emphasis is placed on illustrated diagrams and tables. This approach, coupled with the book's compact size, makes it both a useful training and reference resource. The book contains worked examples of methods discussed and references are provided at the end for further information.

The book may be used by team leaders, chairpersons, supervisors or by lecturing staff to assist in the explanation of HACCP methodology. Specific training support material with tailored worked examples and exercises can be produced by the publisher on request.

**HACCP can be incorporated into ISO 9000 or TQM and may be used as the basis of a due diligence defence.**

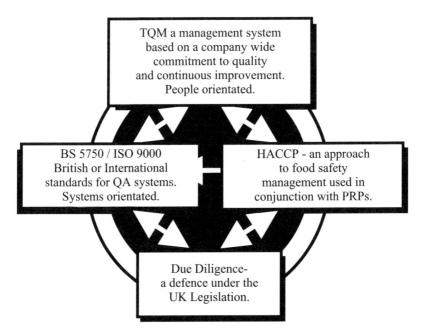

## 0.2. Benefits and Costs of HACCP

**Benefits**

*To the company:-*

- Production of safer food - lower business risk

- Improved / maintained reputation

- Compliance with legislation

- Staff have clearer ideas of food safety requirements and practices

- Demonstrates company commitment to food safety

- Better staff organisation / use of time

- Long term reduction in wastage (in the short term wastage costs may go up due to corrective actions, requiring disposal of food as a result of failure to control CCPs properly)

- Less likely to receive customer complaints
- Possible increase in market access

*To customers:-*

- Less risk of illness
- Improved quality of life
- Greater confidence in food

*To Government:-*

- Facilitating food safety inspections / more efficient food control
- Improved public health / reduced health care costs
- Facilitates international trade

## Costs Associated with implementing HACCP

*Initial / start up costs:-*

- Formal meetings / management costs
- Preparation of background information (e.g. flow charts)
- Staff training
- External consultant fees
- Overtime / pay costs
- Possible equipment costs (e.g. to layout or fabric of the building), in addition to that needed for monitoring and possible design and construction costs*.
- Increased cost of documentation
- Miscellaneous, e.g. travel costs for training

*Implementation costs:-*

- Time spent on monitoring
- Cost of monitoring, e.g. chemical costs - such as ATP bioluminescence monitoring of cleaning

* Arguably these costs, which may be incurred are not truly HACCP costs but relate to having adequate PRPs. However they may be incurred at the time of HACCP implementation.

- Time / money spent on better cleaning

- Costs of corrective actions, if this requires disposal of product

- Ongoing staff training

- Increased maintenance costs, e.g. refrigeration equipment for better temperature control

- Time spent on record keeping

Additional time spent on HACCP may not always translate into real or actual costs, e.g. people do more work or substitute HACCP for other work. Overall costs of initiating and implementing HACCP are affordable even by small businesses. This is especially true when considered in relation to failure costs, e.g. food poisoning fines, compensation, loss of reputation, etc.

**Benefits of HACCP**

Systematic and scientific

Pro-Active and preventative

Cost-Effective

Identifies all conceivable hazards

Focuses technical resources on critical activities

Prevention = Reduced Losses

Complements other QM systems

Internationally acknowledged (FAO/WHO, CODEX)

Due Diligence support

Applicable throughout the food chain

Greater confidence in product safety

Safety introduced in product development

## 0.3. Key Definitions.

# What is HACCP?

**H** a z a r d
**A** n a l y s i s
**C** r i t i c a l
**C** o n t r o l
**P** o i n t s

"Systematic approach to the identification and assessment of the hazards and risks associated with a food operation and the defining of the means of their control."

# RISK

"The chance [probability] that a given hazard will occur."
* Judgement of risk should be made so that level of concern for CCP can be made."

# Critical Control Point (CCP)

"A point, step or procedure at which control can be applied and a food safety hazard can be prevented, eliminated or reduced to an acceptable level."

# HAZARDS

A potential to cause harm to the consumer (Safety).

"Specific Threat"
E.g. Staphylcoccal Enterotoxin, Salmonella

"Operational Malpractice"
Cross contamination

# Examples

| Bacteria | Salmonella, Listeria |
| Toxins | Aflatoxins |
| Viruses | Hepatitis A |
| Parasites | Tapeworm, Trichinella |
| Chemical | Pesticides, |
| Foreign Bodies | Glass, Metal, Insects |
| Biochemical Changes | Histamine |

# Control Measures

Activities that eliminate hazards or reduce occurrence to an acceptable level.

# Monitoring

Observations or measurements to assess whether control measures at a critical point are being implemented effectively.

# Critical Limit

The value of a control measure, determined during monitoring, that distinguishes acceptable and unacceptable.

A complete list of definitions can be found in Appendix 1 and should be consulted before attempting to draw up a HACCP plan.

## 0.4. Preparing for HACCP

Introducing HACCP or revising an existing HACCP scheme, "like robbing a bank", requires care in preparation and planning.

Phase 1 concerns preparation of those activities in advance of sitting down to construct the HACCP plans.

Introducing HACCP into a company for the first time is likely to involve a major change to the way things are managed, how successful this introduction will be is dependent upon the skills of the HACCP project co-ordinator or team leader. This person requires process and technical skills - process here refers to managerial and interpersonal skills such as ability to lead, manage. Technical skills relate to food safety and product knowledge as well as scheduling, budgeting, etc.

### Phases of HACCP Implementation

**Phase 1** *Prepare it*
*Preparation - getting ready*

**Phase 2** *Plan it*
*Designing the HACCP plan - Codex principles*

**Phase 3** *Use it*
*Implementing the HACCP plan*

**Phase 4** *Prove it*
*Maintaining the HACCP plan*

**HACCP Implementation**

The introduction of HACCP, in spite of any legislative requirements, may be met with resistance or antagonism just because it is different.

## Reasons for Resistance to Introduction of HACCP

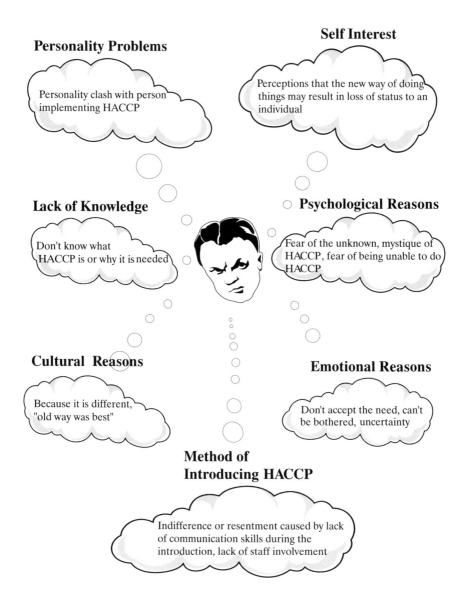

**Personality Problems**

Personality clash with person implementing HACCP

**Self Interest**

Perceptions that the new way of doing things may result in loss of status to an individual

**Lack of Knowledge**

Don't know what HACCP is or why it is needed

**Psychological Reasons**

Fear of the unknown, mystique of HACCP, fear of being unable to do HACCP

**Cultural Reasons**

Because it is different, "old way was best"

**Emotional Reasons**

Don't accept the need, can't be bothered, uncertainty

**Method of Introducing HACCP**

Indifference or resentment caused by lack of communication skills during the introduction, lack of staff involvement

## 0.5. Preparation Activities

It is the responsibility of senior management to appoint and support a HACCP Leader. They should select an appropriate trained person with necessary technical and managerial skills, and provide financial and administrative requirements.

**HACCP team leader should:**

**Communicate with senior management to provide information on:**

- Progress intentions, objectives etc.

- Maintain management commitment to the process

**Skills audit:**

- Identify in house expertise

- Recommend and identify *external consultants if necessary

- Identify information "gaps" and sources of information and any training needs

- Consult training co-ordinator, personnel department if applicable

**Verify accuracy of pre-requisite programmes:**

- Confirm existence adequacy and implementation of the following:

- Cleaning and Sanitation

- Personal Hygiene

- Training

- Traceability and Recall

- Premises Design and Construction

- Pest Control

- Supplier Specification and Control

- Raw Material Control

- Chemical Control

**Prepare for Producing HACCP Plan:**

- Plan meetings
- Produce Gantt chart
- Define PERT analysis, etc.
- Ensure relevant data available for team, e.g. physical complaints records
- Decide if HACCP microbiological data software will be needed

**Obtain required level of Staff support e.g. secretarial, administrative:**

- Select Staff

*Role of external consultant is to assist in house staff. Beware of any consultant who says they will do it all for you!*

**Potential team members/section leaders should:**

**Participate in HACCP Team**

- Ensure any necessary training is undertaken
- Communicate with other staff in their section
- Check that PRPs in their section are adequate and implemented
- Check that records are available

**All:**

**Communication:**

- Ensure that all staff are informed of what is happening
- Need for HACCP and benefits
- Inform work force (and union if applicable)

Strategies for overcoming any resistance are presented in table 0.4.1 although not all of these will be needed on all occasions. Some are more useful than others within specific circumstances.

### Table 0.4.1 Strategies for overcoming resistance

| | |
|---|---|
| Education and Training | Essential to convey techniques and benefits of HACCP. A UK HACCP training standard at intermediate and advanced level is now available (Royal Institute of Public Health and Hygiene). Food safety / hygiene training is necessary to ensure fundamental PRPs are covered. Project management / team building training. |
| Communications | 360° passage of information - from top management to part-time cleaning staff and back upwards. Legislation needs. |
| Participation and Involvement | May need to set up working groups, task forces, focus groups, quality circles, consultation as well as HACCP team. |
| Help and Support | Support groups / networking, open atmosphere, use of external consultants, training, generic HACCP plans, training packs. |
| Negotiations and Agreement | Important if trade unions became involved. Changed practices may be perceived as more skilled with additional pay. It may be good practice, as part of an incentive to make HACCP succeed, to reward training and participation, etc. with financial incentives (increases motivation). |
| Manipulation / Coercion | May represent confrontation - a final resort which in some cases is necessary. Manipulation is more subtle trying to influence events behind the scene, e.g. if one member maybe problematic (with influence over others) get them to join the HACCP team so they are part of the change. Coercion may involve direct threats if people refuse to participate. |

## Table 0.4.2  Barriers to implementing HACCP

| | |
|---|---|
| Lack of finance and resources | Especially in small business. Recent studies suggest costs of HACCP whilst proportionally greater for small businesses are affordable. Time may often be more of a problem than direct cash costs. |
| Lack of government commitment | This is likely to become less of a problem in the future. Increasingly HACCP is recognised as the best way to improve food safety. Within the EC, HACCP principles are incorporated into EC directive 93/43. Codex recommendations advocate use of HACCP plus international agreed principles (Alinorm 97/13A, Appendix II). Trend for HACCP to be mandatory in many countries for most sectors e.g. USA, New Zealand, Canada - GATT and WTP agreements on equivalence of food safety systems. Greater government pressure to include food service establishments especially where tourism is important. |
| Lack of customer and business demand | Reports from many countries of tourists (up to 50% in some countries) suffering gastrointestinal infections with greater liability on the travel operators to use 'safe' hotels. Greater demand on suppliers by retailers and manufacturers. |
| Human resource constraints | Lack of skilled workforce. More HACCP courses to an agreed training standard will help to correct this. |
| Lack of technical support | More books, consultants, training packages and information on hazards and risk. Government guides to implementation. |
| Inadequate support and facilities | Older poorly designed factories are likely to be phased out for economic reasons. Still likely to remain a major problem in some developing countries and some food service establishments. |
| Inadequate communications | Still a major problem for smaller companies / food service and developing countries. |
| Staff resistance | See table 0.4.1 |
| Staff time | Time is an important factor in both designing and maintaining a HACCP plan (see HACCP Costs). |

## Process or Project Management Skills

Scheduling the construction of the HACCP plan will help to make the process of development and implementation much easier. This requires taking the various stages of HACCP (see 0.6) - listing the activities, deciding upon the order, duration and timing of the various activities and arranging necessary resources. A range of simple techniques can make these tasks easier, e.g. Gantt charts, PERT, load analysis, etc. and can provide a "visual" plan which can be analysed and modified to achieve maximum efficiency.

| Agenda | | |
|---|---|---|
| **Start Time** | | |
| Topic | Time Allowed | Person responsible |
| Equipment Hygiene<br>Equipment Maintenance | 30 mins<br>30 mins | QA<br>Engineering |
| **Finish Time** **Total Time** | 1 Hour | |
| **Follow-up Required** | | |
| Topic | Due Date | Person responsible |

**Ensure commitment of company directors.**

The owner of the business must be aware of the time, money and person days required for the project to be completed. In a small company the owner may be part of the team. Larger companies will require a clear presentation of a simple HACCP development plan.

**\* Collect relevant background information - this information is particularly useful at stage 7 to identify significant hazards.**

i    Customer complaint data, QC results and specifications.

ii   Existing product flow diagram.

iii  Contact local enforcement officers and national agencies for information e.g. food poisoning statistics.

iv   Contact local Trade Association for information on particular sector and availability of specialist support if needed.

## Gantt chart and Resource Planner

The Gantt chart below illustrates the detailed plan for development of CCP procedures which is one stage in the overall development of the HACCP plan.

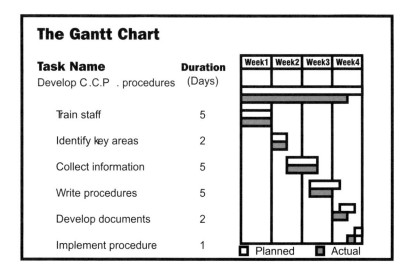

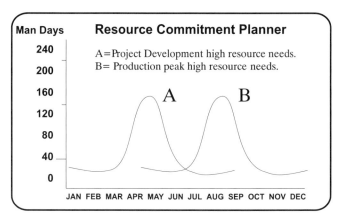

Gantt charts allow the manager to plan and monitor suggested activities and time. The resource planner can be used to plot manpower usage against time and ensure that the resources are optimum and not committed at the busiest time of the year.

**0.6. HACCP Principles.**

The many activities involved in constructing a HACCP plan will be discussed in detail. The following 7 principles should be used and considered by anyone involved in HACCP.

**1  Conduct Hazard Analysis**

**2  Determine CCPs**

**3  Establish target levels and critical limits**

**4  Establish monitoring procedures**

**5  Establish corrective actions**

**6  Establish verification**

**7  Establish documentation**

## 0.7. The Fourteen Stages of HACCP.

It is possible to implement the seven principles of HACCP in 14 separate stages. The Codex documentation identifies 12 stages or logic sequence, an additional stage has been added at the beginning and end within the UK HACCP approach. The approach outlined here reflects the sequence of the Codex documentation with verification procedures preceding record keeping. The stages are presented in outline form in this section and will be discussed in greater depth in subsequent sections. Appendix 9 contains the latest Codex thoughts on implementing HACCP.

1. Define the terms of reference Choose the product and start with safety hazards

2. Assemble a HACCP team - if relevant

3. Describe the product - attach label

4. Identify intended use

5. Construct a flow diagram

6. Confirm on site

7. Identify and list all relevant hazards and control measures

8  Determine CCPs

9  Establish target levels and critical limits for each CCP

10  Establish monitoring system

11  Establish  corrective action plan

12  Establish verification procedures

13  Establish documentation and record keeping

14  Review HACCP plan

## Stage 1 : Define the Terms of Reference/Scope of the Plan.

### 1.1. Getting Started.

It is all too easy when starting to construct a HACCP plan to be over ambitious. It is better to complete a simple HACCP plan which can be expanded later than a complex plan which is never implemented or finished. Therefore, the terms of reference should be outlined clearly at the outset. Decide upon the process line, product and whether physical, chemical and microbiological hazards are to be considered. When developing a HACCP plan for the first time, consideration of only one of these types of hazard is often more practical.

The end point of the plan also needs to be defined, i.e. does the plan finish when the food leaves the factory? Initially this may be simpler and the plan may be subsequently developed to include reasonable expected abuse at later stages e.g. by retailers, caterers or consumers.

### 1.2. Checklist.

☑☒ Specify product/process

☑☒ Clarify hazard category (Microbiological, Chemical, Physical)

☑☒ Safety or quality

☑☒ Safe at consumption or manufacture

   : Prioritise safety

   : Kiss. Keep it simple

## Stage 2 : Select and Assemble a Team.

### 2.1. Team Requirements.

Assembling the team provides a useful opportunity to motivate and inform employees about HACCP. Team selection should be done by the chairperson or an external HACCP specialist. It is essential to get the right blend of expertise as the team will collect, collate and evaluate technical data, and identify hazards and critical control points. People typically involved include quality assurance/control staff, production personnel, an engineer and a microbiologist. In smaller companies, one person may fulfil several roles or even constitute the whole team. In the latter case use of external consultants or advice may be necessary.

Ideally the team should not be larger than about six although additional members may be co-opted when necessary. The team should have some initial training in HACCP. Adequate financial and human resources should be available to the team.

### 2.2. Checklist.

☑ Wide range of data - need multiskills

☑ QA / QC understands the hazards and risks

☑ Production specialists - process expert

☑ Engineer - Hygienic design and Operation of plant

☑ Chairperson - HACCP experience

☑ Adequate resources

☑ Training

## Stage 3 : Describe the Product.

### 3.1. Understanding/Knowing the Product.

The HACCP team need to have as complete an understanding of the product as possible. All details of the product's composition and processing should be known and understood. This information will be essential for microbiological hazards because the product's composition needs to be judged in relation to the ability of different pathogens to grow (Stage 7). This can be summarised as:

**Know your friends (the food - its composition and processing).**

**Know your enemies (the hazards - their severity and risk).**

The following structured checklists can help the HACCP team to record comprehensive information although small businesses may only be able to complete the general checklist.

### 3.2. Checklist (General Checklist)

**Full description of product requires knowledge of the following:**

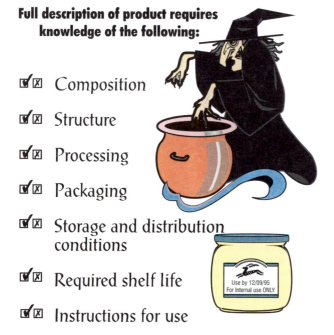

☑☒  Composition

☑☒  Structure

☑☒  Processing

☑☒  Packaging

☑☒  Storage and distribution conditions

☑☒  Required shelf life

☑☒  Instructions for use

## 3.3. Formulation of Recipe Checklist.

☑ ☒ What raw materials or ingredients are used?

☑ ☒ Are micro organisms of concern likely to be present on or in these materials, and if so what are they?

☑ ☒ Do any of the ingredients have toxic properties or contain toxic substances?

☑ ☒ If preservatives are used, are they at concentrations able to prevent the growth of microbes of concern?

☑ ☒ Are any of the ingredients used in quantities too high or too low for culinary needs?

☑ ☒ Will the pH of the product prevent microbial growth or inactivate particular pathogens?

☑ ☒ Will the $a_w$ of the product prevent microbial growth?

☑ ☒ What is the Eh of the product?

## 3.4. Processing and Preparation Checklist.

☑ ☒ Can a contaminant reach the product during preparation, processing, or storage?

☑ ☒ Will microorganisms or toxic substances of concern be inactivated during cooking, reheating, or other processes?

☑ ☒ Could any microorganism or toxin of concern contaminate the food after it has been heated?

☑ ☒ Would a more severe processing be acceptable or desirable?

☑ ☒ Is the processing based on scientific data?

☑ ☒ How does the package or container affect survival and/or growth of microorganisms?

☑ ☒ What is the time taken for each step of processing, preparation, storage and display?

☑ ☒ What are the conditions of distribution?

## 3.5. Final Product Checklist.

Final Product Information

Name                                    Date:

General Characteristics

Composition/Raw Materials          Processing Details

Volume

| Functional Information | Value |
|---|---|
| pH | 4.2 |
| Aw | 0.85 |
| Salt content | 3% |
| Etc. | |

Labelling Details - Attach Label

Storage Conditions and shelf life - on site

Distribution Conditions

## 3.6. New Product Development

In designing new products safety needs to be considered prior to launch. If a product cannot be produced safely it should not be produced. Safety, and thus HACCP, need to be considered at the development stage when there is still time to design safety into the product. For example, if necessary lowering the pH or changing the heat processing without affecting sensory properties (thus consumer acceptability) can be used to minimise microbial hazards. Similarly, careful choice of machinery / plant can minimise presence of physical hazards. Drawing up anticipated flow diagrams can illustrate how production could be changed to eliminate or minimise hazards i.e. design in safety, design out hazards and risk.

## Stage 4 : Identify the Intended Use.

### 4.1. Consumer/Target Groups.

It will be useful if you identify who the likely purchasers or consumers of the product are. Some groups of the population, elderly, very young, sick or immuno - compromised are much more susceptible to some hazards. You may need to label appropriately. If there is a risk of Listeria monocytogenes being present, label " not recommended to be eaten during pregnancy". Other examples include specific reactions to the product or its constituents e.g. nuts, azo-dyes, histamine, phenylalanine etc. The intended consumer group may affect the "level of concern".

It will also be of benefit to understand how the food is likely to be handled or abused by consumers.

### 4.2. Checklist.

☑ ☒   Consumer and target groups- this may affect concern level

## Regarding the expected use of prepared foods

☑ ☒   Is the food expected to be held hot, chilled, frozen or at ambient temperature after it leaves the plant or store?

☑ ☒   Will the time-temperature exposure during reheating inactivate microorganisms and toxins of concern?

☑ ☒   If the food is held after reheating, will it be held hot or at ambient temperature?

☑ ☒   Will the food be handled or otherwise exposed to potential contamination?

## Stage 5 : Construct a Flow Diagram.

### 5.1. Product and Work Flow.

It will be much easier to understand the life history of the product if you produce a comprehensive flow diagram.

**"A picture is worth a thousand words."**

It is easier to identify routes of potential contamination, suggest controls and discuss this with others if you are looking at a diagram. The level of pictorial information on a flow diagram can be more detailed, if needed at specific stages, to enable a more thorough discussion.

It is the flow of all raw materials from the point at which they enter the plant, though processing to departure that makes HACCP specific. It is the specificity which makes HACCP powerful and distinguishes it from a general "floors, walls and ceilings inspection" of the premises.

### 5.2 Checklist

☑☒ Focal point of study

☑☒ Format - variable - not fixed

☑☒ Should cover entire process including delays

e.g.

Raw material & pack data-specifications

Floor plan and equipment layout

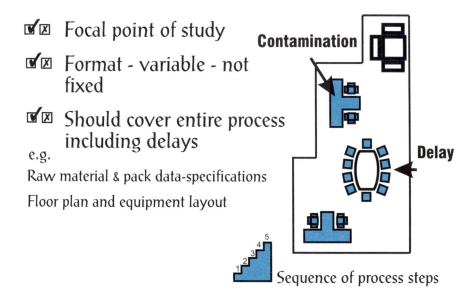

**Contamination**

**Delay**

Sequence of process steps

## Flow Diagram for Cooked Turkey

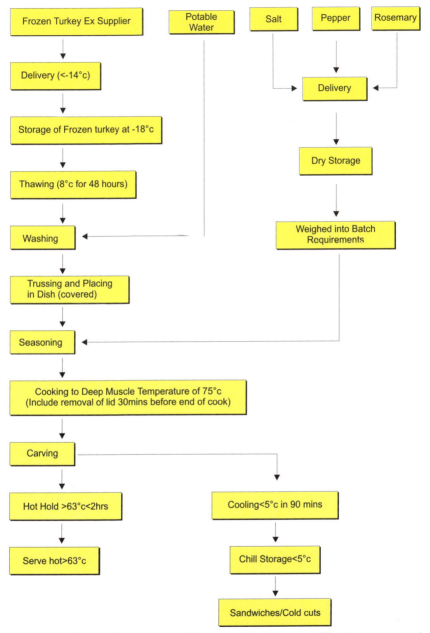

Adapted from Royal Institute of Public Health and Hygiene example paper.

**HACCP Analysis**

The initial steps in analysis involve identifying specific
hazards e.g. staff, and their contamination points in your factory.
Detailed layouts and flow diagrams will assist at stage 7.

# Factory Floor Plan

Product flow

To Store →

Cook/Chill

Hand Fill/Pack

Preparation/ Ingredient
Assembly

Raw Material
Intake

Cold Store 2

Cold
Store 1

Product flow

# Contamination Points

Other types of diagrams may be useful

## Stage 6 : Confirm the Flow Diagram.

### 6.1. Confirming Events.

Once a flow diagram has been produced it needs to be checked for accuracy. Variations in work practices often occur when different line managers are in control, for example small differences can easily occur between one shift and another. The original flow diagram may have been produced from outdated documentation and may not include new machinery which may have been installed. Remember:

**"Because you're mine we walk the line".**

**"You must verify if you have to testify".**

This check will involve all members of the HACCP team and at different times with different shifts and can vary from simple inspection to a completion of comprehensive checklists. The more thorough the assessment the more likely the accuracy of the HACCP plan. The completed checklists can form a record of the assessment and provide a baseline for the assessment of change. Amendments or discrepancies from the original flow diagram should be noted.

### 6.2. Checklist

☑☒  Team confirm  accuracy of flow diagram

☑☒  Include shift patterns and weekends

☑☒  Amend as needed- note deviations

☑☒  Confirm the amended version is correct and produce the final flow diagram

☑☒  Records kept

# Observations from walkabout: Manufacture of baked product

**1.Mixing** — Raw Material (Incoming Goods) — Salt — Yeast — Flour — kg

**2.Fermentation** — 3Hr @ 27°C

**3.Dividing**

**4.Rounding**

**5.Intermediate Proving** — 10-15 minutes rest

**6.Final Moulding**

**7.Final Proof**

**8.Baking**

BakedPFC.cdr

**Comments: Poor handling at proving, Baking time incorrect**

## Stage 7 : Identify & List Relevant Hazards and Control Measures.

### 7.1. Background

This stage is often the first 'problem' for people producing their first HACCP plan, especially if they do not have access to current microbiological information and customer complaint data. Hazard analysis can be defined as, the process of collecting and evaluating information on hazards and conditions leading to their presence in foods to decide which are significant for that food's safety and therefore should be addressed in the HACCP plan. This requires a systematic evaluation of all raw materials used in the food at all the steps identified in the production flow diagram. Thus the hazard analysis is a logical continuation of product description and flow chart construction. As the definition suggests, there are a number of component parts to the hazard analysis. The first lists all the hazards that could be present in the food. The second part is assessing risk (probability and severity) and the final part identifies ways in which the hazards may be controlled. It is at this stage that the chairperson has to ensure the HACCP team stick to their terms of reference. Are all hazards to be identified or only one category e.g. chemical or microbiological? The latter represent the largest known danger to health from food. Additionally, operational malpractices and contamination points, such as improper cleaning, also need to be identified. Identification of hazards should start with raw materials and may finish, for example, with the product leaving the plant, or at the point of consumption.

Once the hazards have been identified, control measures based on a knowledge of the hazards and their normal sources and contamination points can be constructed.

HACCP Analysis

33

## 7.2. Decision Tree for Identifying Potential Microbiological Hazards.

It is often useful for even experienced microbiologists to take a fresh look at their products. The following decision tree may be useful and should be used in conjunction with Appendix 2. Additionally, larger companies can use their own microbiological results and research to assist in their decision making. Appendix 3 contains a fuller discussion of the use and application of decision trees.

## 7.3. Use of Potential Pathogen Decision Tree

One of the most important steps within HACCP is to establish the hazardous organisms that may be associated with a particular food product. The approach presented here is to start with a list of human food pathogens. This is followed by an evaluation of raw materials, the production process, possibilities for contamination etc. This results in deletions from the original list of pathogens. Named pathogens presenting a possible risk are then evaluated in relation to epidemiological data and their ability to cause illness, associated with a specific or related food product. Those remaining pathogens with a low Minimum Infective Dose or not requiring to grow in the food are immediate potential hazards. Those micro-organisms with a higher Minimum Infective Dose or requiring growth receive further consideration. An estimate needs to be made of the likelihood of these organisms growing in the food up to and including consumer use. Thought needs to be given to the role of the consumer and reasonable expected consumer abuse (RECA) as well as product composition and intended storage. This can lead to the identification of some micro-organisms deemed marginal i.e. the risk is present but at a low level. Additional thought then needs to be given to the severity of the illness caused by the organism and the use of the risk severity matrix.

Once the potential pathogens have been listed it becomes possible to identify their main sources and possible contamination routes. This in turn helps to establish control measures.

## Decision tree for identifying pathogenic micro-organisms

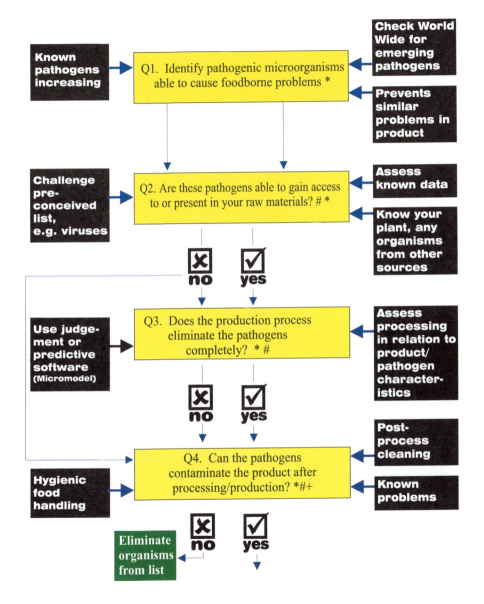

\* Consult the literature or Appendix 2.
\# Perform microbiological tests.
+ Review previous microbiological results.
= Review reasonable expected consumer abuse (RECA).

## Decision tree continued.

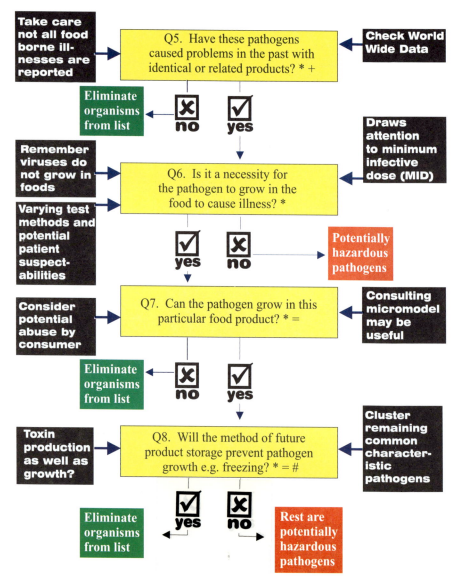

Take care not all food borne illnesses are reported

Q5. Have these pathogens caused problems in the past with identical or related products? * +

Check World Wide Data

Eliminate organisms from list

☒ no  ☑ yes

Remember viruses do not grow in foods

Varying test methods and potential patient suspectabilities

Q6. Is it a necessity for the pathogen to grow in the food to cause illness? *

Draws attention to minimum infective dose (MID)

☑ yes  ☒ no

Potentially hazardous pathogens

Consider potential abuse by consumer

Q7. Can the pathogen grow in this particular food product? * =

Consulting micromodel may be useful

Eliminate organisms from list

☒ no  ☑ yes

Toxin production as well as growth?

Q8. Will the method of future product storage prevent pathogen growth e.g. freezing? * = #

Cluster remaining common characteristic pathogens

Eliminate organisms from list

☑ yes  ☒ no

Rest are potentially hazardous pathogens

* Consult the literature or Appendix 2.
# Perform microbiological tests.
+ Review previous microbiological results.
= Review reasonable expected consumer abuse (RECA).

## 7.4. Physical and Chemical Hazards.

Depending upon the initial terms of reference of the HACCP team, physical and chemical hazards may need to be considered. Appendix 2 contains details of common physical and chemical hazards. Both can be important in food safety and both can give rise to numerous complaints about product quality. Previous customer complaint records, if available, and a company's own quality control records are the most useful sources of information on physical and chemical hazards.

Examples of chemical hazards include cleaning chemicals, pesticides, toxic metals, organic compounds (e.g. PCBs) packaging plasticisers, etc. Contamination with chemical hazards can take place at any time from the farm to consumption. The minimum dose needed for some chemicals to cause acute illness is known but others may have a chronic long term effect following consumption of low levels over extended periods.

A wide variety of physical hazards exist but they can be classified into 5 major categories - glass, metal, wood, plastic and miscellaneous (see Appendix 2 ). Miscellaneous includes items such as sand, paint, stones, rubber, etc. whilst objectionable, foreign matter may not necessarily constitute a hazard. One recent approach has suggested potential criteria for physical hazards as being hard or sharp objects with a length of 7mm or longer. Smaller objects however may constitute a hazard for certain at risk groups, e.g. infants. These criteria apply to ready to eat foods and those requiring only minimal processing which could allow the hazard to persist. Other foreign matter could be considered a physical hazard if it had the ability to cause choking.

## 7.5. Checklist for hazards and controls.

- ☑☒ Flow conditions/ Liquid and solid
- ☑☒ Product recycle/ rework
- ☑☒ Equipment design features (Voids)
- ☑☒ Efficacy of cleaning
- ☑☒ Environmental hygiene

- ☑☒ Personnel routes/hygiene & training
- ☑☒ Route of potential Cross-contamination
- ☑☒ Identification of High/Low risk food & areas
- ☑☒ Storage and Distribution - Consumer instructions

## 7.6. Tools and Techniques Identifying Hazards and Contamination Points.

Once the hazards have been identified it is important to consider how they can be present in the food product. Part of the hazard analysis therefore is the identification of operational malpractices or events that lead to contamination. Two techniques which may be useful in this process are Brainstorming and Cause and Effect Analysis. The aim of both of these techniques is to generate ideas and they can be used separately or together.

### Rules of Brainstorming

| | |
|---|---|
| **1. Topic** | Everyone talking about the same idea. |
| **2. Volume** | More ideas and information the better. |
| **3. Record** | Write everything down. |
| **4. Take Turns** | Let everyone have a say. |
| **5. 1 go per person** | People should not be allowed to dominate the meetings. |
| **6. Pass** | Say "Pass" if you cannot think of anything when its your turn. |
| **7. No criticism** | Attack problems not people. |
| **8. No comments** | Avoid being sidetracked. Concentrate on the job in hand. |
| **9. Wild ideas** | A wild idea may make someone else think of a sensible one. |
| **10. 5W's + 1H** | Who, What, Where, Why, When & How. |

Brainstorming is a technique in which the participants, in turn, state one possible cause of a problem. Observing a few simple rules will help to obtain originality and integration of thinking as well as enthusiasm. Flip charts can be useful recording devices in brainstorming sessions.

## Cause and Effect Analysis

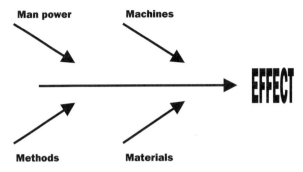

Cause and effect analysis is a technique often used by quality improvement teams and provides an additional structure to brainstorming by grouping ideas together. The effect or problem (e.g. contamination) is represented by a vertical or horizontal arrow or spine, potential principal causes are identified as arrows entering the spine. In turn each principal arrow can have secondary arrows representing sub causes. The end result is a diagram that lists all the causes of a problem with the appearance of a fish bone. The principal causes are often considered under the heading of the 4M's. These stand for:

**Man power**   Skills, training, attitudes, knowledge.

**Method**   Procedures, inspections.

**Machines**   Processing, engineering.

**Materials**   Attributes of the product and its components.

Once a comprehensive fishbone diagram has been constructed, the team attempts to verify the possible causes, identify the most important, and prioritises action.

Brainstorming and cause and effect analysis can be used in a third approach known as Failure Mode and Effect Analysis (FMEA). Using this approach people are asked to suggest possible events (failures) whether they have occurred previously or not. This forms the basis for predicting the future consequences of the failures and whether additional appropriate control measures are needed.

**Part of a Cause and Effect Diagram highlighting the People / Manpower component.**

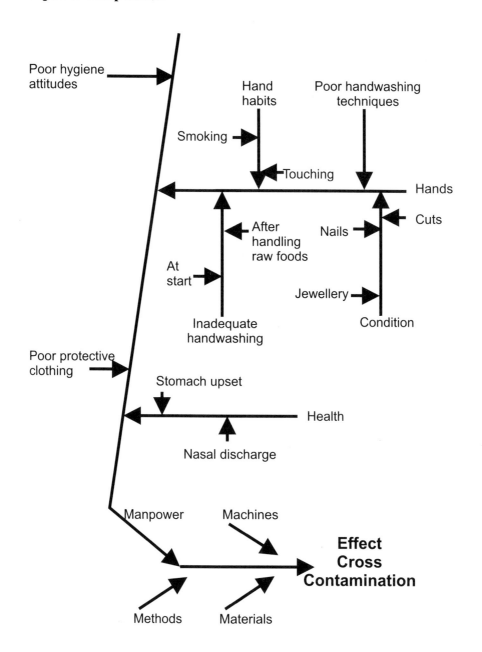

# Potential for Cross-Contamination in Commercial Food Preparation

**Food Raw Materials**

**Cleaning Methods**

**Raw Material Preparation**

**Equipment**

**Environment**

**Post Cooking Handling**

**People and Personal Hygiene**

**The Effect.**

## Cross-Contamination of Ready to Eat Foods

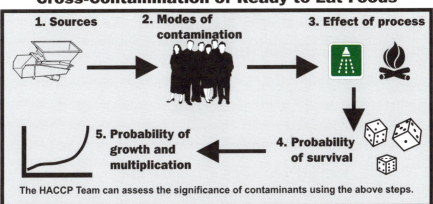

**1. Sources**

**2. Modes of contamination**

**3. Effect of process**

**5. Probability of growth and multiplication**

**4. Probability of survival**

The HACCP Team can assess the significance of contaminants using the above steps.

## 7.7. Risk Assessment.

The terms risk and risk assessment can be used in a wide variety of contexts. We can talk about the risk of somebody being ill after eating a particular food or the risk of a food being contaminated with a particular organism. We can discuss risk assessment of either of these events or we can use it to describe the process of evaluating food premises to decide if they need to be inspected frequently or not. Therefore to avoid confusion, readers should be aware, of the different ways in which the term is used.

Within HACCP the risk concept is used to prioritise actions and determine level of control, and risk can be defined as the likelihood or probability that a hazard will occur with consideration of severity. Attempts can be made to quantify risks mathematically e.g. calculate how often somebody eating chicken is ill, how often listeria can be isolated from a type of cheese or how often salmonella can be isolated from hen's eggs.

This approach requires careful interpretation within HACCP. Often the amount of raw data is inadequate or insufficient. Even if figures are calculated they can be misleading e.g. if a hazard occurs once in every 2000 portions, it does not mean that once the hazard has occurred 1999 more portions can be produced before the hazard occurs again.

An alternative is to consider food risk categories. This can be simple or complex. A simple approach is just to describe the food as belonging to a risk category which can be high, medium or low.

**Category 1 Products (High Risk).**

i.   Products containing, fish, egg, vegetable, cereal and/or dairy ingredients (any substitutes of these) which need to be refrigerated.

ii.  Raw meat, fish and dairy products.

iii. Products with pH values of 4.6 or above that are sterilised in hermetically sealed containers, or sterilised and aseptically filled into sterile hermetically sealable containers for ambient distribution.

iv. Infant formula.

**Category 2 Products (Medium Risk).**

i.  Dried or frozen products containing fish, meat, egg, vegetable or cereal and/or dairy ingredients or any substitutes for these and other products excluded in the food hygiene regulations.

i.  Sandwiches and meat pies for fresh consumption.

iii. Fat-based products e.g. chocolate, margarines, spreads, mayonnaise and dressings.

**Category 3 Products (Low Risk).**

i.  Acid product (pH value below 4.6) such as pickles, fruits, fruit concentrates, fruit juices and acid beverages.

ii. Unprocessed and unpacked raw vegetables.

iii. Jams, marmalades and conserves.

iv. Sugar-based confectionery products.

v.  Edible oils and fats.

**The rationale behind the allocation of foods to these groups is a consideration of:**

*   Is the food product likely to contain and/or support the growth of potential pathogens?

*   Will the product undergo any additional heat processing?

*   Will future storage conditions or handling provide opportunities for the growth of pathogens or further contamination?

*   Is the population consuming the food specially susceptible?

In some cases risk may be combined with the seriousness or severity of the effect of the hazard. Hazards can be described as severe, medium or low (see Appendix 2). Combining risk with severity gives us the degree of concern which is expressed as high, medium, low or negligible. Note that it is possible to have a low risk with a severe hazard giving rise to high concern! An example of this would be manufacturers of canned foods and their concern for botulism. This type of approach can be used to prioritise actions but it does not eliminate the need for action concerning lesser hazards.

Example of Microbiological Risk assessment can be seen in Appendix 8 Risk Profile Example of Staph. aureus and Listeria monocytogenes in cooked ham, adapted from CCFRAG (2000) Guideline 28.

**7.8. Control Measures and Level of Control.**

Once the hazards and how they get into the food (sources and contamination points) have been identified then control measures can be decided. A control measure is the action or activity required to eliminate a hazard or reduce its impact or occurrence to an acceptable level. More than one control measure may be required to control one hazard and more than one hazard may be controlled by one particular control measure. The work on risk assessment in combination with the damage potential (hazard severity) can help to decide upon the level of control to be implemented.

A variation of this approach has been used in Ireland to help in the decision about what is critical and what is not.

Microbiological Risk Assessment (MRA) is a detailed analysis of risk. Figure 7 gives an overview of the steps involved, and illustrates that Exposure Assessment and Hazard Characterisation can be conducted in any order. An example of risk assessment can be seen in Appendices 5 and 8.

MRA forms part of risk analysis, alongside risk management and risk communication. It is this assessment that requires input from microbiologists and involves dealing with knowledge about and information on micro - organisms. Due to the complexity involved in risk assessment, it should only be used to assess one hazard, or type of hazard, at a time for a single product. When MRA and HACCP are used together, they allow companies to minimise risks, which are associated with identified microbiological hazards.

# Figure 7. Microbiological Risk Assessment

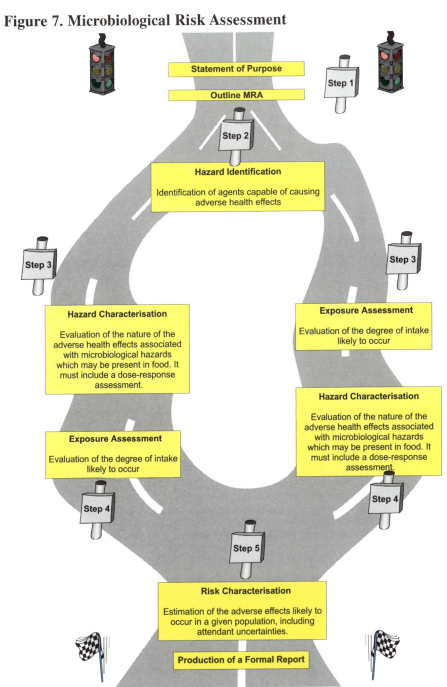

Adapted from Notermans, S. Mead, G.C. and Jouve, J.L. (1996)

## Level of Process Control

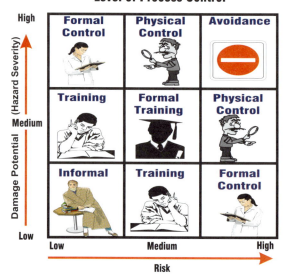

## Determine Level of Control Required

| Example | Risk | Damage Potential | Level of Control |
|---|---|---|---|
| Spoilage bacteria chilled product | Medium | Medium | Formal |
| Damage packaging | Medium | Low | Training |
| Salmonella in raw chicken | High | Low | Formal |
| Botulism in canned food | Low | High | Physical |
| Botulism in cold smoked vacuum fish | High | High | Avoidance |

| | |
|---|---|
| **Avoidance** | Risk and potential consequences are too high to manufacture |
| **Risk** | Estimate of Probability, simple scale Low to High |
| **Damage Potential** | Effect of hazard on business, simple scale low to High |
| **Formal Control** | Compliance with documented criteria, e.g. Start up procedures cleaning programmes, Vendor controls |
| **Physical Control** | As Above by means of continuously monitored physical process e.g. pH, Temperature, Chlorine in water |
| **Informal Control** | Checks or monitoring of a process which may not be recorded |
| **Training** | e.g. Hygiene, Induction, Operational |

46

**A further modification incorporating a points system can also be used.**

### Risk Assessment Matrix.

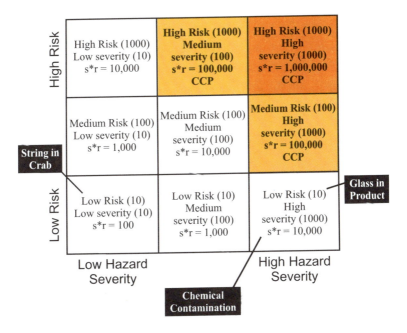

This risk matrix can be used for assessing the "significance" or ranking of hazards, the example shown above illustrates the use of ranking within the preliminary stage of HACCP plan development. Alternatively the risk matrix can be used to screen suspected critical control points to verify that they truly control significant food safety hazards.

Ranking can be used prior to employing the CCP decision tree. The team assess severity by employing appropriate reference data, e.g. Appendix 2, and estimate probability of occurrence by either using generic sector statistics, in-company data or by the judgement of the group. This will formalise the ranking method used and ensure that more consistent decisions and actions are taken.

## Stage 8 : Identify CCPs - Apply the Decision Tree

### 8.1. Background

The HACCP team by now will have completed stages 1-7. A complete list of hazards will have been identified along with how the hazards can contaminate the food, plus a list of possible control measures. If a hazard does not have a control measure then the product or process should be re-designed. It is likely that a large number of control measures will have been identified and for the sake of good manufacturing practice (GMP) it may be desirable to implement many or all of them. The raw material tree can be used to identify "critical" raw materials and ensure that the appropriate preventative measures are included within the final Supplier Quality Assurance system. Worked examples of the raw material decision tree are given in Appendix 3. Not all, however, will be essential for food safety and the next stage in the HACCP is to identify those points in the process at which safety control is critical.

These points can be identified by using the codex decision tree (8.3) or other means and are known as critical control points (CCPs). They highlight for the manufacturer where particular care has to be concentrated in the implementation of control measures. Theoretically there is no limit to the number of CCPs and it will vary considerably on the complexity of the process and the type of product.

It is, however, desirable to keep the number of CCPs to a minimum so that full attention is given to those control measures that are essential for food safety. Examples of the application of the Codex tree are given on pages 50 - 53 and a further discussion is included in Appendix 3. These examples also illustrate the use of the risk matrix in verifying CCPs and also the judgement and experience of the team in deciding on CCPs.

## 8.2. Decision tree to identify raw material - these should be part of the supplier quality assurance programme.

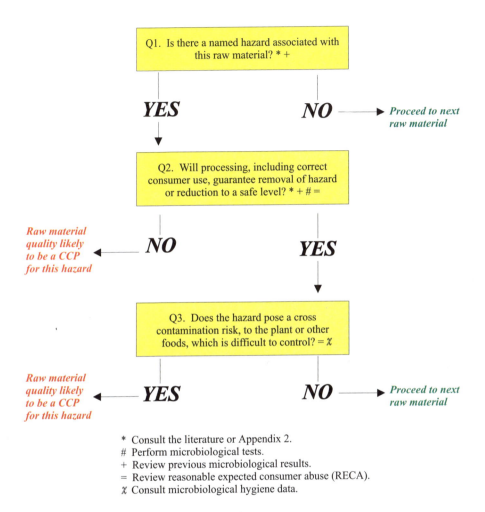

* Consult the literature or Appendix 2.
\# Perform microbiological tests.
\+ Review previous microbiological results.
= Review reasonable expected consumer abuse (RECA).
𝒳 Consult microbiological hygiene data.

See Appendix 3 for worked examples.

## 8.3. The Codex CCP Decision Tree.

The decision tree is a series of questions that the HACCP team ask about each process step plus associated hazards and control measures identified in the flow diagram. The team should record their results on the CCP record chart (see pages 83 - 89 and page 118)

# CCP Decision Tree (Hazards)

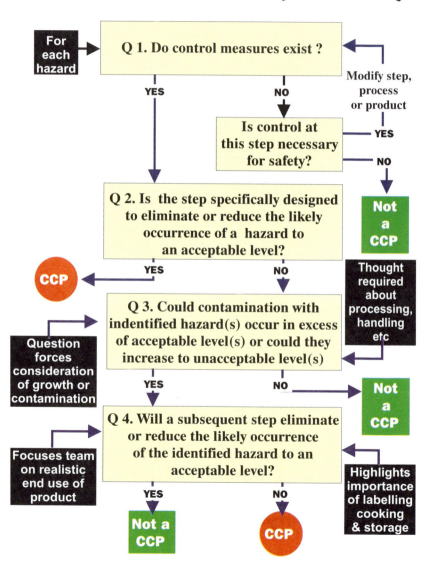

## Decision tree - Question 1

☑☒ Are control measures in place?
Yes - then go to Question 2
No - then ask following questions

☑☒ Is control necessary for product safety?
No - this is not a CCP

## Decision tree - Question 2

☑☒ Does the step eliminate or reduce hazard occurrence to an acceptable level?

At this point the HACCP team will need to consider the details and properties of the hazard as well as the technical composition of the product.

Yes - Then this is a CCP and precisely what is critical should be stated e.g. temperature, chlorine level etc.

No - Go to Question 3

If the identified hazards are microbial then appropriate technical data to review may include pH, aW, preservative type and level, product dimensions and process details.

## Decision tree - Question 3

☑☒ Could contamination occur at unacceptable levels or increase to unacceptable levels?

Team consider flow diagram data, hazard data and use their prior experience.

Do the raw materials (RM) contain any hazard in excess of acceptable limit?

If you are unsure then answer yes - Consider epidemiological evidence and supplier history

Could contamination occur from the environment?

Have we considered the accumulated effect of hazard?

No - this is not a CCP

Yes - Go to Question 4

## Decision tree - Question 4

☑☒ Will a subsequent step eliminate or reduce hazard to acceptable levels?

This is only considered if the answer to Q3-Yes

The team should assess whether the hazard is subsequently controlled

Correct consumer use must be considered

Yes - then this is not a CCP

No - A CCP has been identified. Identify what is critical - Determine preventative measures.

Records may be kept by either completing a blank decision tree/record sheet or by completing a decision tree table as illustrated on pages 83 -89. These may be important in verification and review.

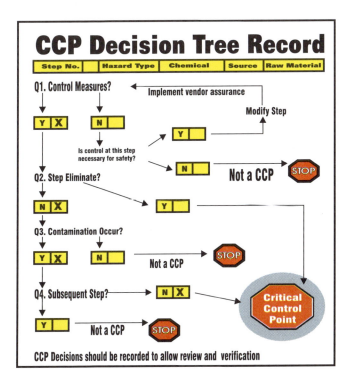

A useful alternative for small businesses can be to apply a simple logic tree (American) with the option of using the Codex decision tree.

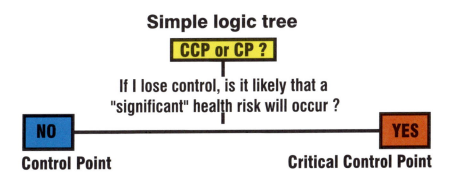

## Stage 9 : Target Values: ATP, Microbiological and Visual Assessment

### 9.1. Background

The HACCP team will now have identified those control measures and specific points which are deemed critical to the safety of the product.

In some cases it will be relatively easy to establish a target value and there may be no critical limit. For example absence of metal of a certain size as determined by a metal detector. The presence of metal indicates unacceptable, absence acceptable, the target is no metal present.

In other instances setting target levels and critical limits is not as easy. For example if the control measure is heat processing, a target temperature has to be selected and the critical limits (acceptable tolerance) stated. Selecting the appropriate temperature will require knowledge of any hazards and their heat sensitivity and also knowledge of the product including pH, surface area, heat penetration data, original temperature, weight and size, see Appendix 2. Time temperature target values can be improved by giving the log reduction or D values (see Appendix 2). The latter may be useful if contamination levels fluctuate. It is essential that technical decisions about targets and critical limits are made by appropriate staff based upon evidence and not arrived at by guesswork. When the HACCP plan is audited the reasons for selected target values will be investigated.

Results from control measures should be obtained rapidly and in time for remedial action to be taken. For example an increasingly used method of determining cleanliness at CCPs is to use luminometry or measurement of ATP.

### 9.2. Using ATP and Microbiological Analysis

Microbiological or ATP testing can be used to confirm cleaning adequacy, however ATP has the advantage of providing results within minutes. Microbiological data can take 24-48 hours. Work needs to be carried out based upon representative diligent cleaning, to establish target levels of cleanliness in terms of cfus and RLUs per cm≈ . Thus the cleaning process is validated, target values and critical limits set and used to monitor cleaning.

Critical limits based upon subjective data e.g. visual inspection, should contain clear specification of the target and examples that are unacceptable. This can be achieved by descriptive statements, photography and charts. Visual assessment e.g. of cleanliness, can often be misleading although visual assessment of other activities e.g. handwashing against specified criteria can be useful.

Other examples of target values can include levels of pH, aW, salt concentration. Often these may interact with one another, e.g. lowering pH can have a synergistic effect on the destructive properties of heat. How to decide on or assess target values is a problem facing many HACCP teams and answers can be based on some or all of the following:

- In- house validation experiments, e.g. heat processing and counting the survival of specific pathogens. More applicable to large manufacturers.

- Published data in books, journals, computer models (Food Micromodel, American Pathogen Model or ICMSF books).

- Expert advice-microbiologists, research associations, EHOs, trade associations, cleaning companies.

Agreement over what can be included as target values is debated amongst HACCP experts with some saying microbiological target values should not be included - mostly due to length of time taken to obtain data. This may be less relevant for raw materials especially if the final product is still on site when the results are obtained. Additionally more rapid microbiological methods are becoming available. Some state "handwashing should not be included due to the level of subjectivity in assessment", although this can be minimised with adequate criteria and training or the use of automated wash stations. However, it is worth remembering that all target values need to be validated. A HACCP team should follow its instincts and evaluate each control measure individually on its merits and be prepared to defend their decision. Any criticism about one individual control measure or activity also needs to be considered within the context of:

*   What are the alternatives?
*   What are the consequences of not specifying the activity as a control measure?

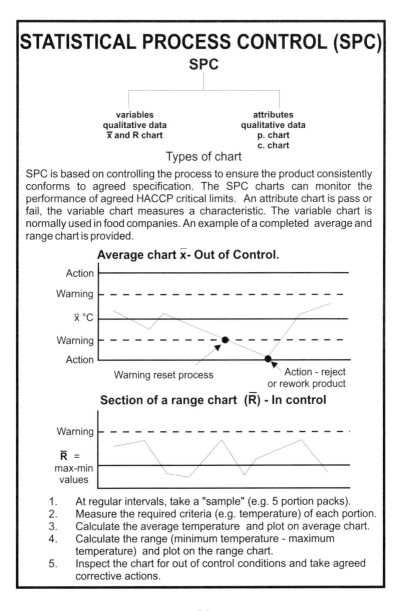

# STATISTICAL PROCESS CONTROL (SPC)

**SPC**

|  variables | attributes |
| --- | --- |
| qualitative data | qualitative data |
| x̄ and R chart | p. chart |
|  | c. chart |

Types of chart

SPC is based on controlling the process to ensure the product consistently conforms to agreed specification. The SPC charts can monitor the performance of agreed HACCP critical limits. An attribute chart is pass or fail, the variable chart measures a characteristic. The variable chart is normally used in food companies. An example of a completed average and range chart is provided.

**Average chart x̄ - Out of Control.**

Action

Warning

x̄ °C

Warning

Action

Warning reset process    Action - reject or rework product

**Section of a range chart (R̄) - In control**

Warning

R̄ = max-min values

1.  At regular intervals, take a "sample" (e.g. 5 portion packs).
2.  Measure the required criteria (e.g. temperature) of each portion.
3.  Calculate the average temperature and plot on average chart.
4.  Calculate the range (minimum temperature - maximum temperature) and plot on the range chart.
5.  Inspect the chart for out of control conditions and take agreed corrective actions.

# Establish a target level and tolerance for each CCP

☑☒  All CCP's identified - now establish levels for control

☑☒  Target level is pre-determined value for control at each CCP with tolerance indicating latitude

☑☒  Examples include temperature, time, moisture, aW, chemical analysis, visual assessment, product and operational practice

## Microbiological target levels

☑☒  Use in house or approved laboratory

☑☒  High risk food may require a control chart

☑☒  Target levels and tolerances should be established for critical areas e.g. raw materials, high risk area, finished product

☑☒  Can results be obtained in time to be useful

## Stage 10:  Establish Monitoring System.

### 10.1. Monitoring.

Monitoring is the series of observations or measurements to ensure that the control measures are being implemented correctly and within critical limits. "If its worth measuring, its worth recording."

Monitoring enables management to detect loss of control at a CCP. Therefore, it is important to fully specify who, how and when monitoring is to be performed and recorded. Results from monitoring should be used pro-actively and illustrate how statistical process control (SPC) can be incorporated into HACCP. For example, results from cleaning (9.2) at a critical control point, can be used to produce a process control chart. Some luminometers include software which automatically record results. These can be plotted to illustrate mean or range values. A low coefficient of variation (CV) indicates the consistency of the cleaning process.

$$\% \ CV = \frac{SD}{mean} \ x \ 100.$$

### 10.2. Ten Commandments of Data Collection.

1   Ask the right questions.

2   Collect appropriate data.

3   Define where to collect.

4   Get an unbiased collector.

5   Help train and equip collector.

6   Keep it simple.

7   Provide instructions (procedure).

8   Test the collection forms.

9   Train collectors.

10  Check the process.

### 10.3. How to Monitor

Monitoring can be continuous where important data is constantly recorded, e.g. temperature graphs for a retort, or can be discontinuous with observations made and then recorded at specific time intervals. A key factor is the length of the intervals and the frequency of monitoring. Too frequent may be cost prohibitive, time consuming and unnecessary. Too infrequent can mean failure to ensure control and possible accumulation of large volumes of suspect product if the next monitoring activity is out of critical limits.

**10.4. Types of monitoring activities**

## Physical
e.g. time / temperature, absence metal

## Observation / visual

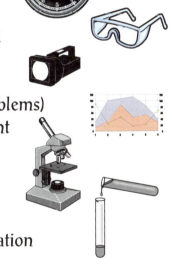

## Microbiological
(may be sampling problems)
• Aerobic colony count
• Coliforms
• Pathogen presence

## Chemical
e.g. pH, salt concentration

Visual inspections may often be poorly carried out and should not be seen as a soft option. They are best performed after training and testing for reliability and reproducibility against very specific criteria which may include photographs, charts, timings, etc. Visual inspection of surface cleanliness should never be used on its own but only as the first part of an integrated approach to monitoring.

## 10.5. Checklist

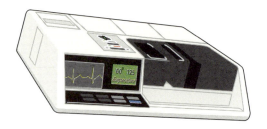

Monitoring methods confirm CCP's are operating within specifications and provides performance records.

☑☒ Systems may be on or off line.

☑☒ Procedures=Who,How & When.

☑☒ Authority confirmed.

☑☒ SPC used or not.

☑☒ Computer or manual information storage.

☑☒ Appropriate training delivered.

## 10.6. Monitoring Procedures and Questions

Is it the correct time to carry out the monitoring?

▼

Are you the right person to carry it out?

▼

Have you been trained, and have the correct instructions/ equipment/facilities/requirements to monitor?

▼

Is there evidence the equipment is sensitive, accurate and precise enough to do the monitoring?

▼

Is the equipment switched on (if applicable) and working correctly?

▼

Is the equipment maintained and calibrated correctly?

▼

Monitor - follow the procedures.

▼

Record results. Compare to target values and critical limits.

▼

Re-monitor if apparent defect or lack of confidence in measurement / assessment and record the actions and reasons.

▼

Implement corrective action if outside critical limit.

## Stage 11 : Establish Corrective Action Plans.

### 11.1. Background

Work completed in Stages 9 and 10 will have specified the tests to be implemented and monitored as well as target levels and critical limits. A corrective action plan describes what should happen if a deviation is found i.e. if the value of a measurement lies outside the critical limit. For this to have happened there must have been a loss of control e.g. failure to achieve a specified pasteurisation temperature or failure to clean properly.

Corrective action plans are also used to specify what should happen if the results obtained at a critical control point are within a critical limit, but trends, e.g. from process control charts, suggest that they soon will be outside i.e. the process is about to go out of control.

### 11.2. Written Action Plan

The action plan should contain details of:

* Immediate action to be taken, who is to be informed and the type of report to be produced.

* What to do with the product that has been produced.

* Investigation of how loss of control has occurred i.e. what has caused the problem and how a recurrence is to be prevented - i.e. how to get the process and future product back under control. Prevention of recurrence should be an essential element of any HACCP plan.

* Who is to assume responsibility for decision making.

Ideally the person who assumes responsibility should have been involved in the original HACCP plan construction. Advice given on what to do with the product, produced under loss of control conditions, should be based on facts or deduction and not guesswork. For microbial hazards, predictive modelling packages e.g. MAFF micromodel, may be useful. A full corrective action plan requires that, either based on experience, prediction or modelling, all the likely problems have been anticipated. Details of how the defective product is handled and whose responsibility it is should be specified. All products that may have been produced since control was lost (last correct monitoring activity) need to be investigated, placed on hold until investigations are complete and re-tested if necessary.

## 11.3. Corrective Actions

Types of corrective actions that can be specified depend upon the hazard, the product, degree of deviation, etc. but include activities designed to ensure the product is back under control and that control of the process is regained.

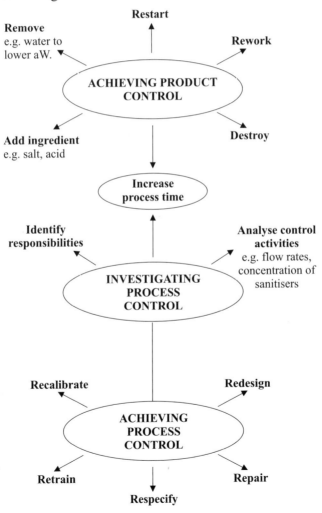

## 11.4. Checklist

☑☒ Specify actions when monitoring indicates unacceptable deviation

Or

☑☒ Specify action WHEN TREND to loss of control

☑☒ Action for disposal of unsafe food or re-work if possible

**Documented procedures WHO, HOW, WHEN**

## Stage 12: Establish Verification Procedures

### 12.1. Background

Verification (principle 6) is defined by Codex as the application of methods, procedures, tests and other evaluations, in addition to monitoring, to determine compliance with the HACCP plan. The NACMSF definition also includes, within verification, checks on the initial validity of the plan, i.e. that it is capable of achieving product safety at the time of design.

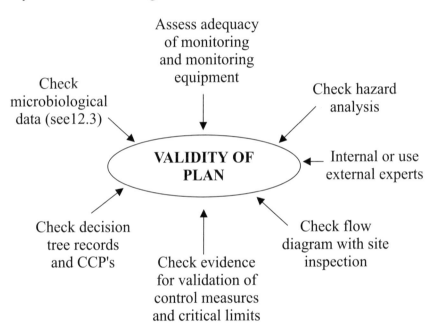

### 12.2. Verification and Audit

**"After HACCP the greatest hazard can be complacency"**

Quote from a Dutch restaurant owner with poor food handling practices.

**"HACCP, yes we have got one of those"**

This last quotation illustrates that once a HACCP plan has been constructed and validated (found to be working) it needs to be implemented, monitored and verified, i.e. that it remains adequate. HACCP plans do not remain in nice folder/binders on a shelf, and only taken down to show people when they ask. They should become a new working way of life with regular assessments of validity including new or emerging hazards, epidemiological data on risk factors, new data on pathogen characteristics, etc. Auditing is an important way of verifying HACCP plans. Auditing a HACCP plan can be defined as:

"A systematic and independent examination to determine whether HACCP activities and related results comply with planned arrangements and whether those arrangements are implemented effectively and are suitable to achieve objectives."

**Auditing can achieve the following:**

- Reinforce and demonstrate food safety awareness
- Assess overall effectiveness of HACCP activities
- Assess compliance with the HACCP plan
- Identify weakness in the HACCP plan
- Analyse level of control at specific critical control points
- Inform management
- Identify areas for improvement
- Incorporate new data into plan
- Confirm that records are kept and available
- Confirm that corrective action procedures are followed and adequate

**Types of HACCP audit**

- 1st Party     Internal (in house auditors)
- 2nd Party     External (e.g. supplier)
- 3rd Party     Regulatory (e.g. EHO audit of butcher's HACCP plan)

For more data references of verification of Listeria see Appendix 2.

| No. | Standard / Element / *Requirement* | Score | | | | | Look At | Look For |
|---|---|---|---|---|---|---|---|---|
| | | 0 | 1 | 2 | 3 | 4 | | |
| 10.0 | **Equipment and Tray Washing** | | | | | | | |
| 10.1 | In-adequate cleaning leading to cross contamination | | | | | | Hygiene Manual O | Hygiene P & R |
| | | | | | | | Maintenance Schedule O | Maintenance P & R |
| | | | | | | | Automatic and manual cleaning systems | Operational std minimses build up of debris |
| | | | | | | | operated with correct chemicals | Reduced facilitation of cross contamination |
| | | | | | | | | Washing equipment subjected to hygiene cleaning (int. and ext.) |
| | | | | | | | | Clean performed in logical manner |
| | | | | | | | | i.e. pre-clean, rinse, foam, rinse, sanitise, rinse |
| 10.2 | Cross contamination of cleaned equipment from dirty equipment | | | | | | Hygiene Manual O | Hygiene P & R |
| | | | | | | | Correct flow from clean to dirty O | Equipment not re-contaminated O |
| | | | | | | | Designated area for clean storage O | Equipment moved to clean area O |
| 10.3 | Aerosols created during washing | | | | | | Washing sited away from production | Hygiene P & R |
| | | | | | | | Air extraction hood | Segregation of cleaning O |
| | | | | | | | | ~roduction of aerosols R |
| ~.0 | **Personnel** | | | | | | | ~ R |
| | | | | | | | | ~quipment and clothing O |
| | | | | | | | | ~ntaminants (listeria) V |
| | | | | | | | | ~ P & R |

## 12.3. Microbiological Examination.

Microbial examination and analysis of both intermediate and final products can play a very important role in verification. The results obtained, especially if combined with computerised storage of data and trend analysis, can be very useful. They can indicate if the HACCP process is working and, if cross referenced to other data, can help to match loss of control with possible causes. Counts of end products before the introduction of HACCP tend to be much higher and more variable. If HACCP is being implemented correctly and is working, counts should be lower and much more consistent (show a lower coefficient of variation). It is likely therefore that the main use of microbiological product testing will change from its historical role of product release/clearance to verification of HACCP, raw materials testing and providing information for use in the decision trees e.g. on effectiveness of control measures.

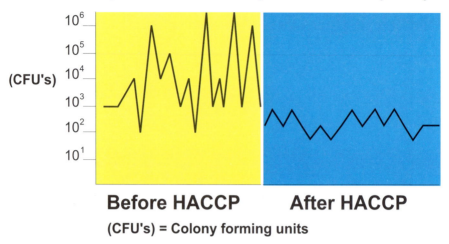

**End product aerobic plate counts (APC)**

Before HACCP        After HACCP

(CFU's) = Colony forming units

## 12.4. Audit Approach

A common technique to guide the audit is to complete a check list. The check list for HACCP audit should focus on the hazard analysis and the critical points, a framework for completion of the check list is provided. The auditor must consider all the parts of the process when constructing a checklist. The full production chain can be viewed as a series of "Units" undertaking specific tasks. These units will consist of up to four elements for the task to be undertaken correctly, these are:

Person        someone to perform or supervise the task.

Item        something on which to work.

Equipment    tools and facilities.

Information    Software or knowledge received or regenerated.

The unit concept can assist in developing detailed checklists.

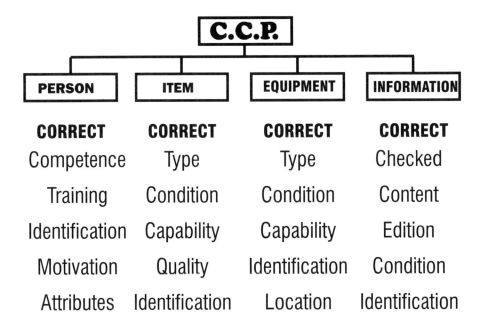

**C.C.P.**

| PERSON | ITEM | EQUIPMENT | INFORMATION |
|---|---|---|---|
| **CORRECT** | **CORRECT** | **CORRECT** | **CORRECT** |
| Competence | Type | Type | Checked |
| Training | Condition | Condition | Content |
| Identification | Capability | Capability | Edition |
| Motivation | Quality | Identification | Condition |
| Attributes | Identification | Location | Identification |

# PLANNING AUDITS

**No. of Key Activities per CCP** **= 4**

## 30 minutes per Activity

## 4 x 0.5Hrs = 2 Hrs to Audit CCP

# World Health Organisation. HACCP Evaluation

**Suggested role of regulatory authority in verification**

**1. Access to records for CCP's - action for non-conformance and corrective action**

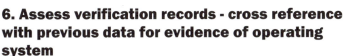

**2. Assess HACCP plan for food safety only**

**3. Assess verification inspection schedules at CCP's - based on degree of risk**

**4. Observation of system to confirm work practice**

**5. Sampling at CCPs or other key areas to independently assure effective control**

**6. Assess verification records - cross reference with previous data for evidence of operating system**

**7. Validation records assessed to ensure HACCP plan reflects product flow and factory layout**

**8. Review of records of actions when changes to HACCP plan have been triggered**

**12.5. Verification Checklist**

**Systems to ensure HACCP is effectively working.**

| STAGES IN AUDIT |
| --- |
| O PLANNING |
| O PERFORMANCE |
| O REPORTING |
| O FOLLOW UP |

☑☒ Is HACCP as originally applied still appropriate to product/ process hazards

☑☒ Are specified monitoring procedures and corrective actions still being applied

☑☒ Team specify METHOD and FREQUENCY of verification

☑☒ May include internal audit, microbiological viable count of a finished product before and after introducing HACCP Microbiological analysis for specific pathogens

See Appendix 7 for further information.

## Stage 13: Establish Documentation and Record Keeping

### 13.1. Background

Efficient and accurate record keeping within HACCP is essential and should provide the manufacturer with confidence that their product is safe and allow auditors to do their job (see 15.4.).

**"I want to be able to sleep at night."** - food manufacturer quote

Auditors may wish to undertake a compliance audit i.e. is the HACCP plan being implemented correctly. Alternatively they may wish to undertake a systems audit i.e. is the HACCP plan appropriate and suitable. For these reasons full details of the component raw materials, the processing and the final product are required. Additionally full details of the HACCP plan, staff training, audit and verification details are needed. A number of software packages exist for computerised record keeping and if they are used, backup copies of data should be made. A person should be designated with responsibility for record keeping.

### 13.2. Checklist - HACCP Documents

**HACCP Documents**

- ☑☒ HACCP plan and any amendments
- ☑☒ Details of HACCP team and meetings
- ☑☒ Data used in validation
- ☑☒ Flow diagrams
- ☑☒ Decision tree data
- ☑☒ Food details - composition, storage, process, use.

**HACCP Records - details / data on**

- ☑☒ Raw materials specifications, supplier certification records
- ☑☒ Monitoring data at CCPs
- ☑☒ Corrective action records
- ☑☒ Findings after corrective action taken
- ☑☒ Monitoring equipment calibration
- ☑☒ Training records
- ☑☒ Previous audit / verification data

**HACCP Documentation Management**

- ☑☒ Documents coded accurately and for ease of accessibility
- ☑☒ Documents filed (old version kept in archives for specific time period in case of need).
- ☑☒ Documents all signed, dated, complete and approved.

Keep Accurate Records

## Stage 14 : Review and Revalidation of HACCP Plan

### 14.1. Background

A review of the HACCP plan is used to determine whether the plan is still appropriate and is additional to the process of verification. Reviews are carried out at predetermined intervals and when changes occur e.g. change in processing, processing equipment or raw materials. Whatever the trigger for the review it is important that the results of review are recorded and fed back into the extant HACCP plan.

| STIMULUS | REASONS |
|---|---|
| New data on old hazards / new hazards | Confirm hazard analysis and that control measures are still appropriate |
| New data on risk factors | Confirm that HACCP plan has adequate breadth, i.e. covers all relevant procedures |
| Epidemiological data indicate a similar type of product is a cause for concern | Confirm HACCP plan is adequate |
| Changes to production process | Confirm flow diagram and validation of control measures |
| Changes to raw materials | Confirm hazard analysis and product composition |

See also Appendix 7

## 14.3. Checklist

The HACCP system triggers review if changes occur to raw materials, product, process consumer group etc.

Examples of triggers include changes in the:

☑☒ Factory layout or environment

☑☒ Cleaning and disinfection programme

☑☒ Processing system

☑☒ Health or spoilage risk associated with product

☑☒ Modification to process equipment

☑☒ New information on hazards/risks

## Stage 15: An Overview of HACCP Development.

### 15.1. Background

An overview of the development of a HACCP system is provided. In this example the HACCP team was divided into two sub-groups-preventing the "technical expertise" of some members from allowing free flow of ideas within the team. A variety of software packages were used to assist in the development of the system and are named below.

### 15.2. Implementation Flow Diagram

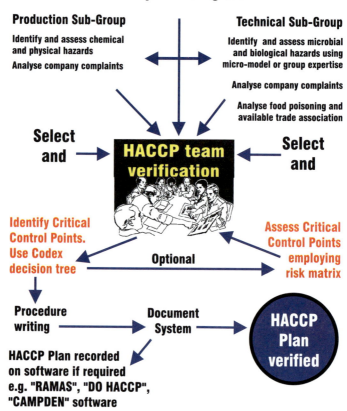

# HACCP Implementation

## Develop flow diagram

**Production Sub-Group**

Identify and assess chemical and physical hazards

Analyse company complaints

**Technical Sub-Group**

Identify and assess microbial and biological hazards using micro-model or group expertise

Analyse company complaints

Analyse food poisoning and available trade association

**Select and** → **HACCP team verification** ← **Select and**

**Identify Critical Control Points. Use Codex decision tree**

**Optional**

**Assess Critical Control Points employing risk matrix**

**Procedure writing** → **Document System** → **HACCP Plan verified**

HACCP Plan recorded on software if required e.g. "RAMAS", "DO HACCP", "CAMPDEN" software

## 15.3. The End Product

The contents and development of a HACCP plan are illustrated below.

# HACCP Plan Worksheet

| 1. | Describe Product |
|----|------------------|

| 2. | Diagram of Process Flow |
|----|-------------------------|

## 3. List Control

| Step | Hazard | Source | Control Measure | CCP(s) | Critical Limit(s) | Monitoring | | | Corrective Action(s) | Records |
|------|--------|--------|-----------------|--------|-------------------|-----|------|-----|----------------------|---------|
|      |        |        |                 |        |                   | How | When | Who |                      |         |
|      |        |        |                 |        |                   |     |      |     |                      |         |

| 4. | Verification |
|----|--------------|

* HACCP Policy
* HACCP on product
* Product information
* Schematic layout
* Flow process
* Schedule for CCP1
* Schedule for CCP2
* Schedule for CCP3
* Copies of referenced procedures and documents

HACCP PLAN

## 15.4. Examples of Documentation of a HACCP Plan for Cooked Chill Crab.

The following sections describe examples of the type of documentation which may be useful in constructing the plan and give an insight into the application of the techniques used to develop the plan. Occasionally CCPs have been reduced to control points after review by the group and in others the CCPs identified at individual steps have been combined. This plan reflects practical decisions generally made in industry and is provided to assist in understanding the practical nature of HACCP systems.

HACCP Policy - cooked chill crab. The Company has a reputation for producing consistently good quality food and enjoy approved status with all the major purchasers as a result of the safety of the products. However the company does not accept this as sufficient proof of due diligence, by extending the consideration given to product safety the company hopes to achieve the following:

i    Confidence that every reasonable precaution has been taken to ensure customer safety.

ii    Acknowledgment by customers and legal authorities, and that the quality systems are based on international standards.

iii    Involvement and awareness of safety by those involved in the preparation of the food products.

**In order to achieve this the Company will:**

i    Complete a full Hazard Analysis investigation on all our product groups.

ii    Ensure that these investigations are validated by customers, local Enforcement officers and by independent expert auditors (e.g. M.D. Associates).

iii    Construct quality systems to ensure that all of the hazards which are identified as being critical are controlled.

iv    Review the effectiveness of these systems and their impact in complaints.

## 15.5. Product Description Cook - Chill Crab.

Crabs which have been caught in approved waters and held in ice prior to transportation to chilled storage. The crab is thoroughly washed and boiled in salt water (5%) at 100°C for 10 mins then plunged in cold water. The shell is then cracked and picking takes place to remove the meat. All operations are performed under hygienic conditions with complete separation of raw and cooked product. The meat is then weighed and packaged, the outer packing being labelled and coded awaiting verification of HACCP plan by positive microbiological tests and then transferred to chilled storage and from there transported to the retail outlets.

**Specification Title. Cook - Chill Crab**
**Specification Code Prod-Std.**

**Quality Control**

| Test Carried Out | Frequency | Final Test before Despatch |
|---|---|---|
| Raw Material | | |
| Organoleptic | Ev 20 min | Yes |
| Colour | Ev 20 min | Yes |
| Physical defects | Ev 20 min | Yes |
| Physical Contaminant | Ev 20 min | Yes |

**Technical Standard - Details**

| | |
|---|---|
| Foreign matter | Absent |
| Shell | <2 pieces/1kg |

Organoleptic To be sweet, tender and free from any objectionable odour or flavour:- to be pink/white in appearance, product which is dark yellow tinged or parts which are inconsistent are unacceptable.

## 15.6. Bacteriological analysis  20g sample each 8 hour shift.

| Test | Satisfactory | Acceptable | Unacceptable |
|------|--------------|------------|--------------|
| APC 30C 48hrs | <25,000 | <50,000 | >50,000 |
| Coliforms VRBA 37C 24hrs | <10 | <100 | >100 |
| Ecoli TBA | <10 | | >10 |

Salmonella (B.Green)        Absent in 25 gms

Listeria FDA /Oxford (Absent in 25 gms)

Certificate to accompany each delivery

## Packaging Description

Crab packed into polythene bags contained in non-returnable cardboard outer with the appropriate coding and appropriate sealing.

## Materials/Dimensions Food Grade Polythene

| | |
|---|---|
| Coding | Not applicable |
| Outer pack | Corrugated cardboard, 200k,150, 200k C flute. Tape sealed |
| Coding | Best before end coded - month/year - processing plus 5 days, plant number and address |

## 15.7. Schematic Layout

The diagram below is an example of the layout for the production of smoked fish and the processing of crab meat before the HACCP programme and team recommendations

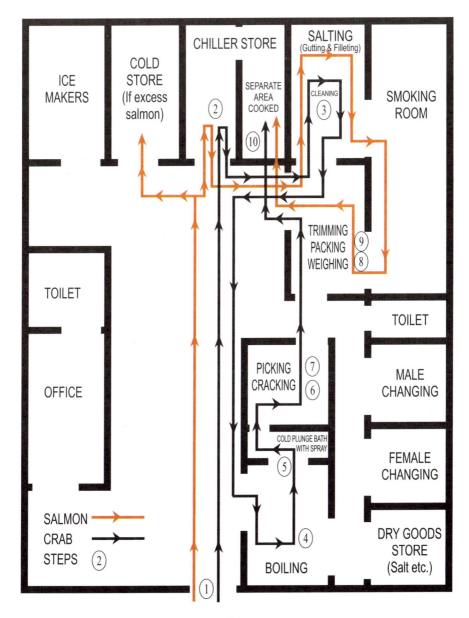

## 15.8. Flow Process

Flow chart diagram showing the processing of crab meat.

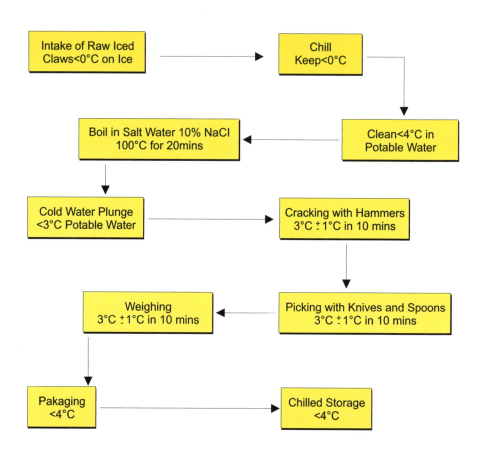

## 14.10. Development of a HACCP plan (cooked crab)

Step 2-9 see crab flow diagram

No control so measures developed

### Hazard Analysis -Physical Hazards

| Process Step & step No. | Hazards | Source | Ranking | Control Measures | Decision Tree Questions 1 | 1a | 2 | 3 | 4 | CCP Yes/No |
|---|---|---|---|---|---|---|---|---|---|---|
| Environment 1-9 | Glass | Lights, bottles, spectacles | High | All glass sources identified and protected from breakage, pre-op compliance check, plant maintenance, visual inspection at packaging | Y | | Y | | | CCP1 |
| Picking | Shell | Cracked | | | N | Y | | | | |
| Picking 7 | Shell | Cracked crab shell | Med | 100% visual inspection under Ultra violet light | Y | | Y | | | CP |
| Environment 1-9 | Metal | Equipment | | | N | Y | | | | |
| Environment 1-9 | Metal | Equipment | Med | Pre-op compliance check, metal detector | Y | | Y | | | CP |

Left as CCP due to high severity & high risk of glass fragments resulting in high ranking

CCP was reduced to CP due to low frequency and medium severity therfore medium ranking

Plant management decided to modify the process to address the problems of shell in the final product by adding an additional control measure i.e. 100% inspection assured by UV light. Further analysis of this hazard resulted in decision to downgrade the CCP to CP as the occurrence of shell was low and only of medium severity , so control point allocated.

**Development of a HACCP plan (cooked crab)**
**Monitoring and control - Physical Hazards.**

| CCP | Control Measures | Target levels Tolerance Limit | Monitoring Procedures | Corrective Action | Record |
|---|---|---|---|---|---|
| CCP 1 (glass) | Pre-op check, plant maintenence | 100% compliance | Preview records of pre-op check | Hold product re-inspection investigate | Audit compliance & maintenance checks |
| CP (shell) | Visual inspection under ultra violet light | no more than 2 pcs greater than 5mm | Control Inspect once/shift | Hold product re-inspection | Inspection records investigate |
| CP (metal) | Pre-op check, metal detector, visual inspection | 100% compliance <2mm Fe <5mm non Fe | Review records of pre-op check, inpect once/shift | Hold product re-test check detector maintenance & investigate | Metal detector test sheets Maintenance records |

## Development of a HACCP plan (cooked crab)
## Hazard Analysis - Chemical Hazards.

| Process Step & step No. | Hazards | Source | Ranking | Control Measures | 1 | 1a | 2 | 3 | 4 | CCP Yes/No |
|---|---|---|---|---|---|---|---|---|---|---|
| Incoming fish | Pesticides | Habitat | Medium |  | N | Y |  |  |  |  |
| Incoming fish 1 | Pesticides | Habitat |  | New source of crab from areas designated as uncontaminated.. SQA - crab suppliers. Random analysis for chemicals & pesticides. | Y |  | N | Y | N | CCP2 |
| Incoming fish | Fuel oil | Boat unloading |  |  | N | Y |  |  |  |  |
| Incoming fish 1 | Fuel oil | Boat unloading | Low | Written specifications to crab suppliers. Sample & analyze crab claws at receipt. | Y |  | N | Y | N | CP |
| Incoming fish | Fuel oil | Ice |  |  | N | Y |  |  |  |  |
| Incoming fish 1 | Fuel oil | Ice | Low | Written ice making procedures. Inspect ice | Y |  | N | Y | N | CP |
| Boiling/cooking | Chemicals | Salt |  |  | N | Y |  |  |  |  |
| Boiling/cooking 4 | Chemicals (cleaning agents) | Salt | Low | Written controls chemical use. | Y |  | N | Y | N | CP |

Decision Tree Questions

Team decided that control is needed

Team decided not a CCP as low frequency & severity therefore low ranking

Testing shown pesticide levels increasing in samples. Decided to keep as CCP although frequency was still low

Team decide control is needed and modify the step

## Development of a HACCP plan (cooked crab)
## Monitoring and Control Chemical Hazards

| CCP | Control Measures | Target levels Tolerance Limit | Monitoring Procedures | Corrective Action | Record |
|---|---|---|---|---|---|
| CCP 2 pesticides | Source of crab, SQA, random analysis | Country standard minus 20% | Audit suppliers, records, random anaysis, verify historical data | Reject shipment, new market, new supply | Analysis records audit records |
| CP Fuel | Written specs, analyze crab/ice at receipt | 0 100% compliance with spec. | Inspection of fish/ice at receipt | Recondition, destroy, retraining | Inspection records Audit records Analysis records |
| CP Chemicals | Written controls chemical use | 0 100% compliance with proceedures | Review cleaning prog, verification of residue by pH paper | Recondition, destroy, retraining | Monitoring record Audit records cleaning schedule |

## Development of a HACCP plan (cooked crab)
## Monitoring and Control - Biological Hazards.

| CCP | Control Measures | Target levels Tolerance Limit | Monitoring Procedures | Corrective Action | Record |
|---|---|---|---|---|---|
| CCP 3 cooking /boiling | Standardized time/ temp process | 20 minute target, 18 minute warning, 16 minute critical limit, load specs | Chart recorder, visual inspection | Reprocess under 16 minute | Time/temp recorded audit records |
| CCP 4 cold water plunge | Chlorinated water, sanitation program, backflow prevention, sanitary zone, employee segregation | 2 ppm target, 1-5 ppm range, 100% compliance to sanitation/ hygiene program | Chlorine check every 4 hours, supervision | Hold/inspect, discipline | Audit record, monitoring & chlorination records |
| CCP 5 cracking picking weighing | Backflow prevention employee segregation sanitation hygiene program time/temp control | Temp - 3°C ±2°C, time - total 30min + 5min, 100% compliance to sanitation prog. | Audit backflow verify layout Medical checks visual inspection ATP checks check time/temp every batch | Hold, re-inspect, check time/temp if exess - freeze and investigate, retrain & report, repair/investigate | Design documents training records Audit records |

## Development of a HACCP plan (cooked Crab)
## Hazard Analysis Biological Hazards (Listeria monocytogenes)

| Process Step & step No. | Hazards | Source | Ranking | Control Measures | Decision Tree Questions | | | | | CCP |
|---|---|---|---|---|---|---|---|---|---|---|
| | | | | | 1 | 1a | 2 | 3 | 4 | Yes/No |
| Incoming fish 1 | Listeria | Raw product | Low | Sanitation, temp control | Y | | | | | CP |
| Cooking/boiling 4 | Survival - growth Listeria | Product | Medium | Standardized time/temp process unit size, incoming temp | Y | Y | | | | CCP 3 |
| Cold water plunge 5 | Contamination/growth Listeria | Water/drains/employees | Medium | Chlorinated water/sanitation progress backflow prevention/sanitary zone | Y | N | Y | N | | CCP 4 |
| Cracking 6 | • | Drains/employees equipment | Very high | Backflow prevention/employee segregation sanitation & hygiene program | Y | | N | Y | N | CCP 5 |
| Picking 7 | • | • | Very high | • | Y | | N | Y | N | CCP 5 |
| Weighing 8 | • | Handling | Very high | • | Y | | N | Y | N | CCP 5 |

Grouped and run as one CCP with in the company HACCP plan as control measures were the same

Testing shows unaccepatable levels of contamination, although a medium ranking the team decides to keep as CCP

Maintained as a CCP with associated measures although the team members gave medium ranking due to low frequency

• = same hazard

The decision to make the cooking step a CCP for Listeria was agreed after much debate. Some team members felt that Listeria posed no "risk" pre-cook and that the measures in place post-cook were the critical areas needing control. The CCP was agreed until the team could demonstrate that no "significant" hazard existed.

## 15.9. Development of the HACCP Schedule.

The HACCP schedule is in two sections, one details the HACCP analysis and the other records monitoring and control information. An example of a completed HACCP schedule for a specific CCP related to cook-chill crab production is given below. The output information from all of the identified CCPs is held within the CCP record section.

## HACCP Schedule - Cook - Chill - Crab

| SECTION 1. | HACCP ANALYSIS | | | |
|---|---|---|---|---|
| Step No. | 1 Potential Hazard | 2 Hazard Source | 3 Control Measure(s) | 4 Critical Control Points(s) |
| Step 7 - Picking Claws | Microbial Contamination | Staff | Hygiene Training Backflow prevention | Step 7 |
| | E.g. Listeria | Drains water | 100% inspection Medical screening | Picking |
| | | | Chlorinated water | CCP 4 |
| **Hazard Type** | **Contamination Source** | | **Control Measures** | **Identified by using CCP decision tree** |

| SECTION 2. MONITORING AND CONTROL - CODEX LAYOUT | | | | |
|---|---|---|---|---|
| 5 Target levels Tolerence Limits | 6 How Monitored | 7 When Monitored | 8 Who Monitors | 9 Corrective Action |
| 100% compliance to sanitation prog. | Training assesment | Annually | Technical manager | Hold/inspect |
| 2 ppm target, 1-5 ppm range, | Chlorine check | every 4 hours | Technical manager | Send to non-risk area |
| Temp 3°C±2°C Time - total 30mins + 5mins | Time/temp probe clock, Audit backflow | every batch | Production supervisor | Freeze, test investigate |
| **Zero tolerance.** | **A time/temp control would have limits.** | | | |

| EXAMPLE OF CCP RECORDS | | | |
|---|---|---|---|
| CCP 1 (Physical) | CCP 2 (Chemical) | CCP 3 (Biological) | CCP 4 (Biological) |
| Audit records, Compliance & maintenance records | Analysis, records, audit records | Time/Temp recorded, audit records | Audit record, monitoring & chlorination records, Time/temp |

# Example HACCP Contents

**Appendices:**

Appendix 1    Definitions.

Appendix 2    Data on Hazards.

Appendix 3    The use of decision trees in HACCP.

Appendix 4    HACCP and Assured Safe Catering (A.S.C.).

Appendix 5    Risk analysis, Risk assessment, HACCP and PRPs.

Appendix 6    Possible CCPs and Common Critical Limits.

Appendix 7    Validation and Verification.

Appendix 8    Microbiological Risk Assessment.

Appendix 9    Guidelines for small less developed businesses (SLDB's) for the application of the HACCP systems.

Appendix 10  Useful references.

## Appendix 1 : Definitions

**Concern** The level of concern is an expression of the seriousness of a failure to control a critical control point. This is derived from the knowledge of a hazard, including its severity and the risk of it occurring. There are different approaches to indicating levels of concern the simplest is:

**High concern** -    Without control it may be life threatening.

**Medium concern** -    A threat to the consumer which must be controlled.

**Low concern** -    Little threat to the consumer but it may be advantageous to control.

**No concern** -    No threat.

**Control** To take all neccesary actions to ensure and maintain compliance with criteria established in the HACCP plan.

**Control Measure** Any action and activity that can be used to prevent or eliminate a food safety hazard or reduce it to an acceptable level.

**Corrective Action** The action to be taken when results of monitoring at a CCP indicates a loss of control.

**Continuous Monitoring** Uninterrupted monitoring of data e.g. non stop temperature, weight or optical density measurements.

**Control Point** Any point or step in a process or procedure at which control can be exercised or applied.

**Critical Control Point (CCP)** Any point or step at which control can be applied and a food safety hazard prevented, eliminated or reduced to an acceptable level.

Note that in the older literature sometimes the terms CCP1 and CCP2 are used. A CCP1 is a critical control point that eliminates a hazard. A CCP2 is a critical control point that minimises but does not eliminate a hazard.

**Critical Limit** The value, of a monitored action (criterion), which separates acceptable from unacceptable.

**Decision Tree (CCP)** A sequence of questions to determine whether a control point is critical or not.

**Decision Tree (Hazards)** A sequence of questions to decide whether a pathogenic microorganism is likely to be potentially hazardous within a food handling or production process.

**Deviation** Failure to meet a critical limit.

**Due Diligence** Section 21 of the Food Safety Act 1990 allows for the defendants to plead that they took all reasonable precautions and exercised all due diligence to avoid the commission of the offence by themselves or persons under their control. The precise precautions and control measures depend upon:

* size and resource of the company
* potential hazards associated with the products
* all other relevant circumstances

**Flow diagram** The detailed sequence of events or steps in any food handling or production process.

**Hazard Analysis** The process of collecting and evaluating information on hazards and conditions leading to their presence to decide which are significant for food safety and therefore should be addressed in the HACCP plan.

**Hazard Analysis Critical Control Point (HACCP)** A systematic approach to food safety which identifies, evaluates and controls hazards which are significant for food safety.

**HACCP Audit (Compliance)** A systematic and independent examination to determine whether the HACCP plan including monitoring, documentation control etc. are being implemented appropriately and complied with.

**HACCP Audit (Systems)** A systematic and independent examination to determine if the HACCP activities are adequate and whether they achieve the intended objectives.

**HACCP Plan** A document prepared in accordance with the principles of HACCP to ensure control of hazards.

**HACCP Review** One aspect of verification in which a documented periodic review of the HACCP plan is made by the HACCP team with the purpose of re-evaluating and if necessary modifying the plan. A review can be indicated for a number of reasons e.g. changes in raw materials, plant layout, new process procedure etc.

**HACCP Team** The team of individuals, usually representing a range of relevant disciplines, who undertake the HACCP study to produce the HACCP plan. Each team is under the leadership of a chairperson.

**Hazard** The potential to cause harm. This may be a specific object e.g. bacteria, toxin, virus, parasite, chemical or physical hazard. Operational malpractices or other operations can also constitute a hazard if they lead to unacceptable contamination or growth and survival of organisms or microorganisms.

**Monitoring** A planned series of observations or measurements of a named parameter, at an identified critical control point. The values obtained should be recorded and compared to the target level and permitted critical limits. The results of monitoring ideally should be obtained rapidly and in time to allow remedial action to be taken if the values were outside the critical limits.

**Preventative Measure** See Control Measure.

**Risk** An estimate of the probability or likely occurrence of a hazard.

**Severity** The seriousness of a Hazard.

**Step** Any location, point, procedure, operation or stage in the food chain including raw materials and/or finished products including stages in production, harvesting, transport formulation, processing, storage etc. as identified in the flow diagram upto final consumption.

**Target Levels** Values of a parameter, at a critical control point, which have been shown to eliminate or control a hazard.

**0** The degree of latitude around a target level that is allowable, i.e. values which are above or below a target level but still within the critical limit.

**Validation** Obtaining evidence that the elements of the HACCP plan are effective, i.e. target values at CCP's are capable of controlling hazards. Also, at the time of HACCP plan design, evidence that it is capable of being effective, i.e. leads to the consistent production of safe foods.

**Verification** Methods, procedures, tests and other evaluations additional to those used in monitoring to determine compliance with the HACCP plan.

**Appendix 2 : Data on Hazards**

## Table 1
## Pathogenic microorganisms able to cause
## foodborne problems, grouped according to hazard severity

| 1.High Severity | 2. Medium Severity | 3. Low Severity |
|---|---|---|
| Clostridium botulinum types A, B, E and F<br>Shigella dysenteriae<br>Salmonella typhi; paratyphi A,B.<br>Trichinella spiralis<br>Brucella melitensis, B. suis<br>Vibrio cholerae O1<br>Vibrio vulnificus<br>Taenia solium (cysticercosis)<br>E coli 0157 | Listeria monocytogenes<br>Salmonella spp., Shigella spp.<br>Campylobacter jejuni<br>Streptococcus pyogenes<br>Rotavirus, Norwalk virus group, SRV<br>Yersinia enterocolitica<br>Entamoeba histolytica<br>Diphyllobothrium latum<br>Ascaris lumbricoides<br>Cryptosporidium parvum<br>Hepatitis A and E, Aeromanas spp.<br>Brucella abortus, Giardia lamblia<br>Plesiomonas shigelloides<br>Vibrio parahaemolyticus | Bacillus cereus<br>Taenia saginata<br>Clostridium perfringens<br>Staphylococcus aureus |

**General guidance note:** The severity of illness will depend upon the specific individual's health and immune system e.g. Listeria monocytogenes can be life threatening for infants but may cause no illness or mild flu like symptoms in adults.

In the above table E coli 0157 has been placed in the high severity column due to its possible effect on young/old people.

## Table 2
## Pathogens / Toxins in General Outbreaks of Foodborne
## Infectious Intestinal Disease 1995/6 in England and Wales

| Organism / Toxin | % of the Total |
|---|---|
| Salmonella (all) | 51% |
| Salmonella enteritidis | 38% |
| Clostridium perfringens | 11% |
| SRSV | 6% |
| Scombrotoxin | 4% |
| Bacillus cereus | 3.5% |
| Escherichia coli 0157 | 3.5% |
| Campylobacter | 1.5% |
| Cryptosporidium | 1.5% |
| Others / Unknown | 16.5% |

NB: This data is for reported cases where the pathogen was identified. Data suggest this is the tip of the iceberg with typically 1 case identified by laboratory based surveillance representing 136 people ill in the community.

The ratio of organisms reported to estimated cases in a UK study of infectious intestinal diseases was 1:3.2 for Salmonella, 1:7.6 for Campylobacter and 1:1500 for SRSV. It should also be noted that in excess of 50,000 notifications of Campylobacter were received but were mostly sporadic and not associated with general outbreaks.

## Table 3

### Food Poisoning Statistics 1980-1999
### (England and Wales) Source OPCS

| Year | Number | Year | Number |
|------|--------|------|--------|
| 1980 | 10318 | 1990 | 52145 |
| 1981 | 9936 | 1991 | 52542 |
| 1982 | 14253 | 1992 | 63347 |
| 1983 | 17735 | 1993 | 68587 |
| 1984 | 20702 | 1994 | 81833 |
| 1985 | 19242 | 1995 | 82041 |
| 1986 | 23948 | 1996 | 83233 |
| 1987 | 29331 | 1997 | 93901 |
| 1988 | 39713 | 1998 | 93932 |
| 1989 | 52492 | 1999 | 86316 |

## Table 4

### Campylobacter (Laboratory Isolations)

| Year | Number | Year | Number |
|------|--------|------|--------|
| 1981 | 12,168 | 1990 | 34,552 |
| 1982 | 12,797 | 1991 | 32,636 |
| 1983 | 17,278 | 1992 | 38,552 |
| 1984 | 21,018 | 1993 | 39,422 |
| 1985 | 23,572 | 1994 | 44,414 |
| 1986 | 24,809 | 1995 | 43,876 |
| 1987 | 27,310 | 1996 | 43,337 |
| 1988 | 28,761 | 1997 | 50,177 |
| 1989 | 32,526 | 1998 | 58,059 |
|      |        | 1999 | 54,994 |

**Note on definitions**

A case of food poisoning or other foodborne illness is a person with symptoms from whom the relevant organism has been isolated or toxin identified or who has symptoms consistent with a known toxic effect or who is part of an outbreak.

An outbreak is defined as two or more related cases of foodborne infection or intoxication. Outbreaks may be family, only the members of one household are affected, or general if more widespread.

# Main pathogenic microorganisms with sources in nature and the foods they are mainly associated with.

| Microorganisms | Source in Nature | Associated Foods |
|---|---|---|
| Clostridium botulinum | Soil, sediment intestinal tracts of fish, mammals, gills, viscera of fish crabs, seafood. | Low-acid canned foods especially home canned. Meats, fish, smoked/fermented fish, vegetables, other marine products. |
| Clostridium perfringens | Soil and sediment (widespread), water, intestinal tracts of humans and animals. | Improperly prepared roast beef, turkey, pork, chicken, cooked ground meat and other meat dishes, gravies. soups and sauces. |
| Salmonella spp. | Water, soil, mammals, birds, insects intestinal tracts of animals, especially poultry and swine. | Beef, turkey, pork, chicken eggs and products, meat salads, crabs, shell-fish, chocolate, animal feeds, dried coconut, baked goods and dressings. |
| Listeria monocytogenes | Soil, silage, water and other environmental sources, birds, mammals, and possibly fish and shellfish. | Raw milk, soft cheese, coleslaw ice-cream, raw vegetables, raw meat sausages, raw and cooked poultry, raw and smoked fish, paté. |
| Campylobacter jejuni | Soil, sewage, sludge, untreated waters, intestinal tracts of chickens, turkeys, cattle, swine, rodents and some wild birds. | Raw milk, chicken, other meats and meat products. |
| Staphylococcus aureus | Hands, throats and nasal passages of humans, common on animal hides. | Ham, turkey, chicken, pork, roast beef, eggs, salads (e.g. egg, chicken, potato, macaroni), bakery products, cream-filled pastries, luncheon meats, milk and dairy products. |
| Shigella spp. | Polluted water and intestinal tracts of humans and other primates. | Milk and dairy products, raw vegetables, poultry and salads (e.g. potato, tuna, shrimp, macaroni and chicken). |
| Vibrio parahaemolyticus | Estuarine and marine waters. | Raw, improperly cooked or cooked recontaminated fish, shellfish, or crustacea. |
| Vibrio cholerae 01 | Untreated water intestinal tracts of humans | Shell fish, raw fish, and crustacea |
| Bacillus cereus | Soils, sediments, dust, water, vegetation and a variety of foods, cereals, dried foods, spices, | Meats, vegetable dishes, milk, cream pastries, soups and puddings.notably  Fried Boiled or cooked rice and other starchy foods (e.g. potatoes and pasta) |

cont.

| Microorganisms | Source in Nature | Associated Foods |
|---|---|---|
| Yersinia enterocolitica | Soil, natural waters, intestinal tracts of various animals (pigs, birds, dogs and cats) | Fresh meat and meat (particularly swine), fresh vegetables, milk, and milk products. |
| Escherichia coli (Enterovirulent types) | Intestinal tracts of humans and animals. | Raw or rare meats and and poultry, raw milk and products, unprocessed cheese, salads.<br><br>Contaminated and unpasteurised fruit juice |

## Table 5
## Reported food vehicles in general outbreaks of food poisoning confirmed by microbiological, statistical or descriptive evidence 1995/6 in England & Wales

| Food | %Outbreaks (rounded up or down to whole figures) |
|---|---|
| Eggs (raw / lightly cooked) | 20% |
| Poultry | 20% |
| Red meat / products | 15% |
| Fish | 7% |
| Rice dishes | 6% |
| Salads / veg / fruits | 6% |
| Milk / dairy products | 4% |
| Bivalve shellfish | 3% |
| Other shellfish | 3% |
| Water | 1% |
| Miscellaneous (sandwiches, pasta, etc) | 13% |

Food vehicles vary between countries and HACCP teams can obtain guidance from international data but should concentrate on local foods and data.

# Table 6
# Growth characteristics and MID of the major microorganisms

| Bacteria or Mould | Growth temp. range °C | Growth pH range | Eh | Max. brine level % | Min. aw level | Compet- ative ability | MID |
|---|---|---|---|---|---|---|---|
| Campylobacter jejuni | 25 - 46 | 4.9-9.5 | MA | 3.5 | NK | Poor | $<10,^{6}$ possibly as low as $5 \times 10^{2}$ |
| Salmonella species | 5 - 47 | 4.0-9.0 | FA | 8.0 | 0.95 | Poor | Variable typically $10^{5}$ |
| Clostridium perfringens | 10 - 50 | 5-8.9 | An | 6 | 0.93 | Poor * | $7 \times 10^{5}$ |
| Staphylococcus aureus | 7 - 48 | 4-10.0 | FA | 17 | 0.86 | Poor ** | Approx.51ug toxin |
| Listeria monocytogenes | 0 - 45 | 4.4-9.5 | A or NA | 10 | 0.92 | Poor *** | NK Probably low for susceptible or immuno- compromised |
| Bacillus cereus | 5 - 50 | 4.4-9.3 | FA | 10 | 0.91 | Poor | $10^{3}$ |
| Vibrio para- haemolyticus | 3 - 43 | 4.5-11.0 | FA | 8 | 0.94 | Poor | $10^{4}$ |
| Escherichia .coli | 3 - 46 | 4.4-9.5 | FA | 8 | 0.95 | Poor | $10^{5}$ |
| Clostridium botulinum | 4 - 48 | 4.6-9.0 | An | 10 | 0.94 | Poor | 5 ng. toxin |
| Yersinia enterocolitica | 0 - 44 | 4.6-9.0 | FA | 10 | 0.94 | Poor | NK |
| Toxigenic Moulds | -12 - 55 | 1.7-11.0 | A | 20 | 0.62 | Poor | Low |
| Food Viruses | NA | NA | NA | NA | NA | NA | Possibly 100 |

**Notes on Table 6**

**1.Abbreviations**

| | |
|---|---|
| MA | Microaerophilic |
| NK | Not Known |
| FA | Facultative Anaerobe |
| An | Anaerobe |
| A | Aerobe |
| NA | Not Applicable (viruses do not grow in foods only in living cells). |
| MID | Minimum Infective Dose (lowest number of organisms or amount of toxin to make you ill.) |
| aw | Water activity. |
| pH | Measure of acidity or alkalinity ($-\log 10$ H+). |
| Eh | This is a measure of the food's oxidation/reduction potential. Eh can be measured in millivolts (mv). Foods with a high Eh (+ 200mv) are oxidised and provide a good growth medium for aerobic organisms. Foods with a low Eh (- 200mv) are reduced and provide a good growth medium for anaerobe. The Eh of foods can change as a result of processing (e.g. heating), chemical changes (e.g. rigor mortis) or other reasons. |
| D value | Time taken in minutes or seconds, at a specified temperature, to reduce the number of organisms by 1 log value (i.e. by 90%). |

**2.** All these values can be extremely variable and are indicative only.

**3.** Values given (except D values) are for growth and not for survival. Organisms can often survive conditions of pH, temp, aw etc. well outside their requirements for growth.

**4.** The ability to grow or survive is dependent on all the other environmental conditions e.g. temperature for growth is dependent on the pH, similarly temperature to kill an organism is dependent on pH. All environmental factors interact and an organism's ability to grow is variable depending upon all conditions for growth. Predictive modelling packages can be useful in deciding if growth will or will not take place.

**5.** Foods themselves vary considerably. Some particulate foods in sauces may show variations upto 1.0 pH value. Surface temperature may differ from centre temperature.

**6.** MIDs will vary considerably depending upon strain of organism, environmental conditions in the food and an individual's susceptibility.

**7.** Competitive abilities. Normally most of the pathogens do not compete well with the other microorganisms present. If given any type of selective advantage this changes.

\*     Clostridium perfringens in an anaerobic environment and other suitable conditions can grow very rapidly, possibly as quickly as doubling every 12 minutes.

\*\*     Staphylococcus aureus although typically slower growing can predominate in high concentrations of salt or lower aw levels.

\*\*\*     Listeria monocytogenes has good abilities to grow at lower temperature and can be selected out by refrigeration.

## Table 7
## Approximate pH value and water
## activity (aw) of some common foods

| Food | pH Range | aw |
|------|----------|-----|
| Poultry | 6.2 - 6.4 | 0.985 |
| Fish | 6.6 - 6.8 | 0.985 |
| Milk | 6.3 - 6.8 | 0.98 - 0.99 |
| Mayonnaise | 3.0 - 3.8 | 0.92 - 0.93 |
| Beef (Ground) | 5.1 - 6.2 | 0.98 |
| Ham | 5.9 - 6.1 | 0.85 - 0.95 |
| Cheese | 4.9 - 5.9 | 0.85 - 0.92 |
| Cooked chill meal* | 4.0 - 6.5 | 0.95 - 0.98 |

* Particularly variable depending on the type and composition of the sauce and the amount of particulate matter (i.e solid : liquid ratio).

## Table 8
## Types of Chemical Hazards

| 1. Naturally occuring chemicals | 2. Added chemicals |
|--------------------------------|--------------------|
| Mycotoxins (e.g. aflatoxin, patulin)<br>Scombrotoxin (histamine)<br>Ciguatoxin<br>Mushroom toxins<br>Shellfish toxins<br>Paralytic shellfish poisoning (PSP)<br>Diarrheic shellfish poisoning (DSP)<br>Neurotoxic shellfish poisoning (NSP)<br>Amnesic shellfish poisoning (ASP)<br>Pyrrolizidine alkaloids<br>Phytohemagglutinin<br>Polychlorinated biphenyls (PCBs) | Agricultural chemical<br>   Pesticides, fungicides, fertilizers, insecticides,<br>   antibiotics and growth hormones<br>   Toxic heavy metals<br>   Lead, zinc, arsenic, mercury and cyanide.<br>Food additives<br>   Direct-allowable limits under GMPs.<br>Preservatives (nitrite and sulfiting agents)<br>   Flavour enhancers (monosodium glutamate)<br>   Nutritional additives (niacin)<br>   Colour additives<br>Secondary direct and indirect<br>   Plant chemicals (e.g. lubricants, cleaners,<br>   sanitizers, cleaning compounds, coating and<br>   paint)<br>Chemicals intentionally added (sabotage) |

**Destruction of Microorganisms by Heat**

Heat energy can destroy microorganisms and is a function of the temperature and the length of time at that temperature. Microorganisms exposed to temperatures, above their maximum for growth will be destroyed although this can be very variable depending upon condition e.g. pH, salt or fat content. As the temperature increases so the length of time required to destroy organisms decreases. The heat energy produced by the time temperature combinations in table 12 is the same and is designed to destroy the most heat resistant non sporing pathogen in milk.

**Table 9**
**Time/Temperature combinations for pasteurisation of milk**

| Temperature | Time Required |
| --- | --- |
| 63°C | 30 mins |
| 71.7°C | 15.0 secs |
| 89°C | 1.0 secs |
| 94°C | 0.1 secs |
| 100°C | 0.01 secs |

The Thermal Death Time (TDT) can be defined as the time necessary to kill a given number of organisms at a specified temperature and although data is available describing TDT's, care must be used in their interpretation. Factors influencing how easily microorganisms can be destroyed by heat include:

i   Nature of the food including its water, fat, salt, protein, carbohydrates content and its pH.

ii  The organisms including their numbers, age and phase of growth.

**Table 10**
**Destruction of E.coli in foods using heat.**

| Food | Thermal death point |
|------|---------------------|
| Cream | 73°C |
| Whole milk | 69°C |
| Skimmed Milk | 65°C |

The table above indicates the effect of the surrounding medium on the destruction of one strain of E. coli. Alternatively a more useful means of describing heat sensitivity/resistance is the D value of an organism (see Table 12). This stands for the Decimal Reduction Time and is the time required at a specified temperature to kill 90% of the organisms present, as temperature increases the D value decreases.

**Table 11**
**Decrease in numbers of Bacteria in food with a**
**D value of 2 mins at 70°C**

| Numbers of Bacteria | Time |
|---------------------|------|
| 100,000 | 0 mins |
| 10,000 | 2 mins |
| 1,000 | 4 mins |
| 100 | 6 mins |
| 10 | 8 mins |
| 1 | 10 mins |

Typical minimum time/temperature processing or cooking for the coolest point in order to kill vegetative pathogens include 70°C for 2 mins or a minimum temperature of 74°C. The latter assumes if the temperature is reached, sufficient heat energy will have been imparted. Cooking typically attempts to attain a 5D reduction (5 log kill) of microorganisms in the food. If the vegetative forms of Clostridium botulinum are suspected this should be increased to 90°C for 10 mins. To remove spores of Clostridium botulinum the "Botulinum Cook" is required i.e. minimum of 121°C for 3 mins (12D reduction).

## Table 12
## Some Typical D Values of Pathogens at varying temperatures under a variety of conditions.

| ORGANISM | D VALUE |
|---|---|
| Campylobacter jejuni | 1 min at 55°C |
| Salmonella species | 10 - 25 secs at 65.5°C<br>0.5 - 5 secs at 71.6°C |
| Clostridium perfringens | spores 1 - 20 min<br>at 100°C |
| Staphlyococcus aureus | 12 - 120 secs at 65.5°C<br>4 secs at 71.7°C |
| Listeria monocytogenes | 5 - 8 mins at 60°C<br>3 - 10 secs at 71.7°C<br>(very variable) |
| Bacillus cereus spores | 5 - 8 mins at 100°C |
| Vibrio parahaemolyticus | 1 - 60 mins at 47°C |
| Escherichia coli | 6 secs at 65°C<br>2 secs at 71.7°C |
| Clostridium botulinum | 0.2 - 1.0 secs at 100°C |
| Yersinia enterocolitica | 6 secs at 48°C |
| Food Virus | 5 secs at 62°C |

**Table 13**
**Important physical hazards and their possible sources**

| Material | Sources |
|---|---|
| Glass. | Bottles, jars, light fixtures, utensils, gauge covers. |
| Wood. | Fields, pallets, boxes, buildings. |
| Stones. | Fields, buildings. |
| Metal including nuts, bolts, paperclips, staples | Machinery, equipment, wire, employees, packaging. |
| Insects and other filth. | Fields, plant post-process entry |
| Insulation. | Building materials. |
| Bone. | Fields, improper plant processing. |
| Plastic. | Fields, plant packaging materials, pallets, employees. |
| Elastic bands. | Packaging, employees. |
| Personal effects. e.g. | |
| Jewellery | Employees. |
| Paper/cardboard | Packaging, employees. |
| Cigarette ends. | Employees. |
| Flaked paint. | Machinery. |
| String. | Packaging |
| Hair. | Employees, animal hides. |

## Possible Contamination

# GLASS

| Possible Origins | Control Measures |
| --- | --- |
| Fragments from Jars and Bottles Broken in Process | Conveyers of open containers should be covered to prevent glass access. Adequate sieving or other separation techniques must be adopted to winnow out broken containers. Try to obtain ingredients in plastic containers. Ensure adequate sieving post decanting. NEVER decant from glass next to the production line. |
| Fragments from Imperfect Jars and Bottles (Blisters) | High frequency audio (or other technique) should be used prior to filling to ensure the absence of imperfections. Try to obtain air extraction for ingredients in bottles - this is far more gentle than using untensils. |
| Light Bulbs and Fluorescent Tubes | All light fittings over production lines should be covered with perspex (or equivalent). During bulb changing, the production line should cease operation and be covered if possible. |
| Sight Tubes and Protective Plate Glasses, Inspection Ports | Remove sight glasses where possible and use remote sensing equipment. If this is not possible, instigate regular documented checks on those sights over production lines. |

## Possible Contamination

# METAL

| Possible Origins | Control Measures |
| --- | --- |
| Nuts, bolts, washers, rivets and roves etc. | Regular documented machinery inspections and preventative maintenance by trained engineers / Inspections by production supervisors following engineering work. |
| Welding spelter, welding scale, welding rod. | Isolation of all welding activities from the immediate environment / Thorough cleaning and inspections following welding activities. |
| Filings and swarf. | Regular preventative maintenance targeting those areas prone to wear / improve segregation between lubricated moving parts, and any food contact surface. |
| Rust flakes. | Use stainless steel wherever possible for food contact machinery / Increase re-coating frequency of mild steel items / Increase frequency of inspection of rust-susceptible areas. |

## Possible Contamination
# RUBBER AND PLASTICS

| Possible Origins | Control Measures |
|---|---|
| Hermetic Seals on Plant and Control Instruments | Regular machinery maintenance. Ensure items are removed from the production area whenever possible for maintenance. |
| Elastic Bands | Thorough inspection of raw materials, coupled with supplier assurance / auditing. Do not allow elastic bands into production areas for wrapping or containment purposes. |
| Foamed Plastic, Soft or Rigid for Insulation | Ensure that any engineering work involving such foam is carried out in down time and the area is subsequently thoroughly cleaned. Minimise the use of such foam near production areas for 'quick fixes'. |
| Plastic Tags, Labels, Dymo Tapes | Use only metal detectable tags or labels. Try and work with systems which do not require such tags and labels. Account for all tags / labels entering and leaving production areas. |
| Cellulose Tape, Insulating Tape | If such tape is required for joining packaging films etc, ensure its use is thoroughly controlled. Use a non-food colour if possible. |

## Possible Contamination
# WOOD

| Possible Origins | Control Measures |
|---|---|
| Fragments from Pallets and Boxes etc. | Incoming goods checks involving packaging condition. Ensure goods arriving on pallets and in boxes are decanted onto plastic pallets or into plastic bins on arrival. |
| Cutting and Chopping Work Surfaces | Use only plastic chopping boards and replace regularly to remove plastic foreign body risks. |
| Stirring Paddles | Replace wooden paddles with plastic or stainless steel alternatives. |
| Twigs, Stalks, Bark and General EVM in Raw Materials. | Audit suppliers of 'high risk' raw materials to vet their seiving and screening processes. Instigate documented spot inspections on samples of dried raw materials likely to contain such foreign bodies. |
| Doors, Door Frames and General Structural Wood | Try to phase out structural wood. In the meantime use documented checks to assess the integrity of any wooden structure on or near production lines. |

## Verification Checklist

### Verification of Listeria spp. Control

**Key to Abbreviations**

| | | |
|---|---|---|
| D – Defined | P – Procedure | O – Observation |
| F – Process Flow | R – Records | V – Visual look at |
| M - Manual | CS – Contact Surfaces | CYAG – Clean As You Go |
| | | DC – Design Control |
| | | C - Control |

| No. | Standard / Element / Requirement | Score 0 1 2 3 4 | Look At | Look For |
|---|---|---|---|---|
| 1.0 | **Floors** Damaged areas that can act as traps/reservoirs for debris and water (ponding), allowing Listeria spp. to multiply | | Hygiene P & M<br>Standing Water (ponds) V<br><br>Floor surface V | Cleaning Operation D<br>Water Use and Utilisation C & R<br>Water minimisation programme P<br>Excess water and standing water C<br>Damage Repair P and R |
| 2.0 | **Drains** Damaged areas that can act as traps/reservoirs for Listeria spp. Product debris trapped under drain cover Overflow/blocked drain leading to excess contaminated water flooding the production environment. | | Hygiene P & M<br>Traps and Drains V<br>Standing Water (ponds) V<br>Drain Flow and Product Debris V<br><br>Drain Repair and Maintenance V | Cleaning schedule and verification of clean<br>Prevent Overflow of drains<br>Blockages cleared and sanitised, not using high press. hoses<br>Water Use and Utilisation P<br>Water minimisation programme P<br>Drain flow takes product from high care to low care O<br>Removal of drain cover during cleaning and manually cleaned O<br>Easily accessible drains for easy maintenance and cleaning P & O |
| 3.0 | **Ceilings, Walls and Overheads** Damaged areas that act as traps for debris and bacteria and contamination sources to the production environment | | Hygiene P and M<br>Maintenance P & R<br><br>Pipes, Ducts and Gantries O | Cleaning Schedules<br>Ceilings and wall surfaces in good state of repair incl. joints Maintained<br>Exposed overheads minimised and within appropriate covers |
| 4.0 | **Cleaning Equipment** Contamination build-up leading to sources of high numbers of Listeria spp. with Aerosol spread by use of hoses or by spread or re-contamination by vectors | | Maintenance P & R<br>Hygiene P and M<br>Cleaned after use and properly stored dry or immersed in sanitiser bath<br>Storage areas - O | Equipment M, P & R<br><br>Equipment used for floors and drains is separated from equipment used for cleaning CS.<br>Defined use of disposable cleaning vectors to minimise contamin.<br>Hoses kept clean and stored off the floor, not used during prod. |

## Verification of Listeria spp. Control

**Key to Abbreviations**

| | | | |
|---|---|---|---|
| D – Defined | P – Procedure | O – Observation | DC – Design Control |
| F – Process Flow | R – Records | V – Visual look at | C - Control |
| M - Manual | CS – Contact Surfaces | CYAG – Clean As You Go | |

| No. | Standard / Element / Requirement | Score (0 1 2 3 4) | Look At | Look For |
|---|---|---|---|---|
| 10.0 | **Equipment and Tray Washing** | | | |
| 10.1 | In-adequate cleaning leading to cross contamination | | Hygiene Manual O; Maintenance Schedule O; Automatic and manual cleaning systems operated with correct chemicals | Hygiene P & R; Maintenance P & R; Operational std minimses build up of debris; Reduced facilitation of cross contamination; Washing equipment subjected to hygiene cleaning (int. and ext.); Clean performed in logical manner i.e. pre-clean, rinse, foam, rinse, sanitise, rinse |
| 10.2 | Cross contamination of cleaned equipment from dirty equipment | | Hygiene Manual O; Correct flow from clean to dirty O; Designated area for clean storage O | Hygiene P & R; Equipment not re-contaminated O; Equipment moved to clean area O |
| 10.3 | Aerosols created during washing | | Washing sited away from production; Air extraction hoods to minimise aerosols | Hygiene P & R; Segregation of cleaning O; Non production of aerosols R |
| 11.0 | **Personnel** | | Staff Training Programme; Staff Experience; Roles and Responsibilities | Training P & R; Use of protective equipment and clothing O; Awareness of possible contaminants (listeria) V; Personnel Hygiene Policy O & P & R |
| 12.0 | **Cleaning Procedures** Adequacy for destroying *Listeria* spp. | | Hygiene Manual; Appropriate use of chemicals | Hygiene P & R; Availability of chemical information and suitability R; Diligent in the verification and validation of cleaning controls P & R |

## Verification of Listeria spp. Control

**Key to Abbreviations**

| | | | |
|---|---|---|---|
| D – Defined | P – Procedure | O – Observation | DC – Design Control |
| F – Process Flow | R – Records | V – Visual look at | C - Control |
| M – Manual | CS – Contact Surfaces | CYAG – Clean As You Go | |

| No. | Standard / Element / Requirement | Score 0 1 2 3 4 | Look At | Look For |
|---|---|---|---|---|
| 5.0 | **Floor Contact Items** These items assist the spread of water and bacteria through the environment | | Use of dedicated equipment (if poss.) O Low risk equipment used in low risk areas i.e. pallets, trollies, fork trucks O | Hygiene P & R (including wheels) Restricted use and access to defined areas – P and O |
| 6.0 | **Non-routine equipment** Contamination from external areas | | Equipment Hygiene Equipment dedicated to use P & R | Hygiene P & R Use of appropriate wipes e.g. alcohol wipes for water sensitive items to minimise contamination O Accounting of Tools and external equipment introduced R |
| 7.0 | **Food Contact Surfaces** Cross contamination potential from inadequately cleaned surfaces with product soiling on table, ledges, under conveyors, in seals, et cetera | | Cleaning Schedules and Manual O Identify all product contact surfaces O | Hygiene P & R Cleaning surfaces identified & cleaned at agreed frequency P & R Cleaning schedule reflects area of factory and use P & R & O Appropriate equipment dismantling P & O CYAG procedures appropriate to production |
| 8.0 | **Refrigeration Units** Accumulation and dissemination of Listeria spp. via the moist air blown through the units and condensation dripping from pipework | | Cleaning Schedules and Manual O Regular cleaning schedules operated R trays etc are not above exposed product O | Hygiene P & R Allow easy access to cleaning Avoids water collection or drainage (condensate) directly to floor. Efficient insulation of pipes to minimise formation of condensate |
| 9.0 | **Air-Handling Systems** Accumulation and dissemination of Listeria spp. | | Cleaning schedules and frequency Air filtration to a minimum std of 95% removal of 5 μm particles to minimise dust R | Hygiene P & R D to minimise potential to trap dirt or accumulate moisture Air intakes sited to avoid cross contamination from low risk to high risk areas |

## Appendix 3. The use of decision trees in HACCP

### 3.1 Decision Trees in General

**Q1 - Is it essential to use Decision Trees in HACCP?**

A1 - No, but it can be useful and desirable.

**Q2 - Why and How can Decision Trees can be useful?**

A2 - HACCP is all about analysing situations, events and probabilities and, in the end, making decisions based upon appropriate data. Decision Trees are structured sets of questions which, depending upon your answer to one question, direct you towards another question or an outcome. They are useful because they:

- Enable you to make objective decisions rather then subjective (i.e. based upon a rationale rather than a gut feeling).

- Provide transparency to your decision making this may be of value to auditors, customers, enforcement officers etc.

- Ask important questions which may not have occurred to you.

- Make you think about something in a detailed structured way.

- Help you to understand your processes and products.

- Help to prioritise and target actions and resources.

**Q3 - How many HACCP Decision Trees are there?**

A3 - There are 3 Decision Trees described in this booklet

* CCP Decision Tree

* Raw Material Decision Tree

* Decision Tree for identifying potential pathogenic microorganisms.

**Q4 - Is one Decision Tree more important than the others?**

A4 - All are useful but the only one that is recommended by the Codex Commission is the Decision Tree for Critical Control Points (CCP Decision Tree).

**Q5 - Why is it useful to use the CCP Decision Tree?**

A5 - The tendency when constructing a HACCP plan, especially for the first time, is to designate too many points as critical. A review of many HACCP plans from the 1980's illustrate this. It is desirable to keep the number of CCP's to a minimum and use of the CCP Decision Tree helps to identify those points that are truly critical and thus help in this process.

**Q6 - What about the Raw Material Decision Tree?**

A6 - Raw materials and their quality are of concern to all food establishments but only in some instances is this central to the safety of the end product. In such circumstances Supplier Quality Assurance (SQA) is necessary, however it is relatively expensive to implement. To minimise waste of time and effort the Raw Material Decision Tree is a quick and simple exercise to perform and indicates whether SQA is essential or not.

**Q7 - What about the Pathogen Decision Tree, why is it useful?**

A7 - The first practical step in HACCP is to identify potential hazards associated with a particular product. Sometimes the products may be unusual and/or could be imported from another hemisphere. The use of the pathogen decision tree is one approach to identifying microbial hazards and helps to make the process proactive, potential pathogens can be identified before they cause problems. If applied, the Decision Tree forces you to approach the problem of hazard identification from first principles rather from assumptions which may be based upon more limited evidence.

**3.2. Specific comments on using the decision tree for identifying potential microbiological hazards.**

Q1 - The list of known pathogens is increasing and monitoring of pathogens world wide can be useful. New pathogens are 'emerging' and recognition of problems elsewhere in the world may alert you and help to prevent similar problems with your product.

Q2 - In many cases people have not looked. This is likely to be particularly true of foodborne viruses. Care needs to be taken to ensure that the media and cultural conditions for pathogen isolation are appropriate. The second part of the question is necessary to cover cross contamination or human contamination of raw materials after delivery but prior to processing.

Q 3 - This may be more difficult to answer than first thought. The heat sensitivity/resistance of pathogens is known to vary considerably depending upon pH, aw, salt content, fat content etc. Use of predictive modelling packages such as MICROMODEL may help. Data can be conflicting for some pathogens e.g. Listeria sp and all these factors need to be considered again later when setting target values and critical limits.

Q 4 - This question is important as some pathogens are more likely to gain access after processing. Sanitation of equipment and techniques for handling foods after processing are particularly important as some organisms can easily colonise processing equipment and can be difficult to eradicate. One case that illustrated this was Salmonella in baby milk when the post processing source could not be eliminated. The hygiene of food handlers is also critical.

Q 5 - Data from the different countries should be examined, especially if products are imported from another country. Care must also be taken because not all cases of foodborne illnesses are reported and in those cases that are, often the causative organism is not isolated. These aspects of hazard identification should receive additional consideration when HACCP plans are verified or reviewed.

Q 6 - This question draws a distinction between infectious and toxinogenic organisms and relates to the Minimum Infective Dose (MID). This can be difficult to determine due to variation in test methods and varying susceptibilies in potential patients. However, generalisations can be drawn. Remember viruses do not grow in foods.

Q 7 & 8 - These link to question 6 and if toxinogenic bacteria cannot grow they can be eliminated. Consulting micromodel can be useful and potential abuse by consumers must be considered. This question may be vital if product reformulation occurs. A number of well publicised instances have occurred which illustrate this. A pathogen, previously unable to grow, has grown due to changes in product composition e.g. change in acids used in mayonnaise, from acetic to citric. Thought should also be given to the homogeneity of foods in answering this question. Foods usually consist of a variety of microenvironments which can differ quite considerably e.g. retorted curries with a high solid content can have pH variation up to 1.0 between different parts of the pack.

For toxinogenic microorganisms this question needs to be asked with reference to toxin production as well as growth.

It is likely that after using this Decision Tree a considerable number of pathogens will remain identified but remember one method of control often works for a range of pathogens. It may help to cluster pathogens based upon common characteristics.

A risk assessment may help to further reduce the number of organisms on the list providing the limits of risk and pathogen severity are carefully specified.

## 3.3. WORKED EXAMPLES USING DECISION TREES

## EXAMPLE 1

### Output from the use of Codex Decision Tree

| PROCESS STEP | HAZARD | CONTROL MEASURES | DECISION TREE QUESTIONS | | | | | CCP Y / N |
|---|---|---|---|---|---|---|---|---|
| | | | 1 | 1a | 2 | 3 | 4 | |
| Cooking Poultry | Survival of campylobacter and salmonella | Cooking (heating, temperature and time) at or in excess of target value | Y | - | Y | - | - | Y |

Application of the decision tree for the heat processing stage of a poultry product made from raw poultry. The results of the individual questions are recorded as indicated to provide transparency of decision making and can be auditable. Question 1a refers to the question "Is control at this step necessary for safety".

## EXAMPLE 2

### Beefburgers for use in a Catering Establishment

**Question 1** - Is there a named hazard associated with this raw material?

**Response** - Yes - Literature and 'in house' microbiological data indicates potential E.coli 0157 and other heat sensitive pathogens.

**Action** - Proceed to Question 2.

**Question 2** - Will processing, including correct consumer use, guarantee removal of hazard or reduction to a safe level?

**Response** - Yes - Heat during cooking is sufficient to destroy pathogens. Cooking can be controlled and monitored.

**Action** - Proceed to Question 3.

**Question 3** - Does the hazard pose a cross contamination risk, to the plant or other foods?

**Response** - Yes - For this particular catering establishment, it is not possible to segregate with confidence raw product and equipment from cooked product.

**Action**- Assume raw material is a CCP. Proceed to next raw material*.

* NB This process should be repeated on all possible hazards so that appropriate supplier specifications can be constructed and would then need to be repeated for all the raw materials e.g. bun, garnishes, lettuce, onion etc.

### EXAMPLE 3

**Raw chicken for retorted Chicken Curry**

**Question 1** - Is there a named hazard associated with this raw material?

**Response** – Yes - Literature and 'in house' microbiological data indicate a range of potential pathogens e.g. Salmonella sp.

**Action** - Proceed to Question 2

**Question 2** - Will processing, including correct consumer use, guarantee removal of hazard or reduction to a safe level?

**Response** - Yes - Product to receive in excess of 'Botulinum cook*'. Sufficient to kill all pathogens. Heat processing is controlled, monitored and recorded.

**Action** - Proceed to Question 3.

**Question 3** - Does the hazard pose a cross contamination risk to the plant, other foods or equipment?

**Response** - No - Plant operates with strict GMP and complete segregation of raw foods and high care areas.

**Action** - Proceed to next raw material or other hazards in raw chicken.

* NB Botulinum cook equivalent to coldest point in the can receiving a heat of 121° C for a minimum of 3 minutes.

## EXAMPLE 4

**Cooked chicken for use in sandwiches**

**Question 1** - Is there a named hazard associated with this raw material?

**Response** - Yes - Literature suggests possible presence of Listeria monocytogenes.

**Action** - Proceed to Question 2.

**Question 2** - Will processing, including consumer use, guarantee removal of hazard or reduction to a safe level?

**Response** - No - Chicken will not receive any further heat processing only assembly into product.

**Action** - Raw material quality is a CCP and requires supplier quality assurance. Additional hazards need identification to construct supplier specifications. Proceed to next raw material in sandwich.

## EXAMPLE 5

**Raw milk for use in making pasteurised milk**

**Question 1** - Is there a named hazard associated with this raw material?

**Response** - Yes - In house analysis indicates that, in a small number of instances, penicillin is present in the raw milk.

**Action** - Proceed to Question 2.

**Question 2** - Will processing remove hazard or reduce it to a safe level?

**Response** - No - Penicillin residue may persist in final product and give rise to allergic reactions.

**Action** - Raw material is a CCP. Proceed to next hazard or raw material.

## 3.4. WORKED EXAMPLE OF DECISION TREE FOR IDENTIFYING POTENTIAL PATHOGENS

### EXAMPLE 1 - SHEET 1

**Pasteurised Milk**

**Question 1** - Identify pathogenic micro-organisms able to cause foodborne disease.

**Response** - See table 1.

**Action** - Proceed to Question 2.

**Question 2** - Are these pathogens present in your raw materials?

**Response** - Given that it is possible under extreme circumstances to find virtually any pathogen in raw milk, the following present a degree of likely risk of contamination. **Bacillus cereus, Clostridium perfringens,** Salmonella species, Listeria monocytogenes, Campylobacter jejuni, Staphylococcus aureus, Shigella species, **Yersinia enterocolitica, Escherichia coli, Brucella abortus, Cryptosporidium parvum,** Polio virus, Hepatitis A virus, **Mycobacterium tuberculosis,** Various enteroviruses, **Coxiella burnetii,** Toxigenic moulds, **Aeromonas hydrophila.**

**Action** - Proceed to Question 3.

**EXAMPLE 1 - SHEET 2**

**Question 3** - Does the production process eliminate the pathogens completely?

**Response** - Pasteurisation is a process specifically designed to ensure milk is safe to drink. The heat treatment was designed to destroy the most heat resistant non spore forming pathogenic organisms - Mycobacterium tuberculosis and Coxiella burnetii. However the success of the pasteurisation can depend on a range of factors including the number of contaminants. Some evidence suggests Listeria monocytogenes could sometimes survive normal pasteurisation.

**Action** - Proceed to Question 4.

**Question 4** - Can the pathogens contaminate the product after processing?

**Response** - Post pasteurisation can occur with any of these pathogens and is dependent upon standards of hygiene - plant and personal.

**Action** - Proceed to Question 5.

**EXAMPLE 1 - SHEET 3**

**Question 5** - Have the pathogens caused problems in the past with identical or related products?

**Response** - The majority of foodborne illness associated with liquid milk relates to untreated (raw) milk. These cases most commonly involved Salmonella sp and Campylobacter. The minority of outbreaks which involved pasteurised milk were due to defective pasteurisation or to post pasteurisation contamination. Hence the need to control pasteurisation effectively and design and clean plant effectively. Where post pasteurisation contamination occurs, the most common causes are inadequately cleaned bottles and poorly cleaned filters. An outbreak of E.coli 0157 in Scotland in 1994 caused 100 people to fall ill. This was probably due to post- pasteurisation contamination. Epidemiological data for England and Wales for pasteurised milk show that between 1980-1989

| Organism | Outbreaks |
|---|---|
| Campylobacter | 5 |
| Salmonella | 3 |
| Staphylococcus aureus | 2* |
| Yersinia enterocolitica | 2 |
| Listeria monocytogenes | 2** |

**Action** - These 5 pathogens proceed to Question 6.

\* Associated with cheese made from pasteurised milk.

\*\* 2 individual cases not outbreaks.

**EXAMPLE 1 - SHEET 4**

**Question 6** - Is it necessary for the pathogens to grow in the food to cause illness?

**Response** - Campylobacter - No
**Action** - Potentially hazardous pathogen

**Response** - Salmonella - Yes
**Action** - Proceed to Question 7

**Response** - Staphylococcus aureus - Yes
**Action** - Proceed to Question 7

**Response** - Yersinia enterocolitica - Insufficient data (ID) *
**Action** - Assume Potentially hazardous pathogen

**Response** - Listeria monocytogenes - ID *
**Action** - Assume Potentially hazardous pathogen

**Response** - E.coli Yes
**Action** - Proceed to Question 7

**Question 7** - Can the pathogens grow in this particular food?

**Response** - Salmonella - Yes
**Action** - Proceed to Question 8

**Response** - Staphylococcus aureus - Yes
**Action** - Proceed to Question 8

**Question 8** - Will the method of future product storage prevent growth?

**Response** - Milk after pasteurisation must be cooled immediately and then kept below 10°C. Salmonella - some species can grow between 5 - 10°C and the organism is capable of relatively quick growth. Abuse of temperature control in distribution chain not uncommon.

**Action** - Assume potentially hazardous pathogen

## EXAMPLE 1 - SHEET 5

**Response - Staphylococcus aureus.** This causes a toxin type food poisoning and production of toxin requires more favourable conditions than for growth of the organism. Typically in ideal conditions minimum of 106 - 107 cells in milk thought necessary to produce sufficient toxin to cause illness. Organism grows relatively poorly below 10°C, toxin not produced below 10°C. Given that temperature abuse in the food chain can occur, decision for milk could be marginal. Data from USA does not list milk in the top 6 foods associated with Staphylococcus aureus food poisoning, although a recent large scale outbreak involving milk and Staphylococcus aureus did occur in Japan. Maturing during cheese making can last months and could provide conditions for growth of **Staphylococcus aureus.**

**Action** - Risk not considered high as a pathogen for liquid milk but epidemiological data will be monitored. Consider **Staphylococcus aureus** as a potential pathogen in milk used for cheese making.

**Summary** - Potential Pathogens for Pasteurised Milk

**Campylobacter**

**Yersinia enterocoliticas**

**Listeria monocytogenes**

Salmonella sp

**Staphylococcus aureus** if milk used in cheese making.

E.coli

## 3.4. The Codex Alimentarius decision tree for determining CCPS

It is important to remember that the Codex Decision Tree is only a tool to help you find the CCPs for your business. It is no more than that. In drawing up the Decision Tree, Codex was trying to do two things. The first was to produce an internationally agreed tool that could be used all over the world. (Prior to the Codex agreement there was no internationally agreed way of determining CCPs). The second was to produce a universal Decision Tree, i.e. one that would cover all products, all processes and all segments of the food chain. This explains way some of the questions might not seem appropriate to your particular circumstances (for example, Question 2 is needed for operations such as raw meat production where there are no control measures that will totally eliminate hazards such as contamination with bacterial pathogens but where there are measures that can be used to keep these hazards to a minimum). However Codex specifically recognises that their Decision Tree is only a tool and even then only one of a number of other decision trees that might be more appropriate in specific sets of circumstances.

Experience shows that people most often have problems with the Codex Decision Tree when they use it to do things it was not designed to do. For example, it was not designed to be used to determine risk or perform any of the tasks of Risk Assessment.

**How to use the Codex decision tree to determine CCPs.**

The keywords for success in this task are flexibility and common sense. Each step may have one or more hazards. The CCPs are identified by applying the HACCP decision tree to each hazard in turn (N.B. it is important to stress that it is each particular hazard that is run through the decision tree). When all the hazards for a particular step have been dealt with, the hazards at the next step in the flow diagram are considered in sequence.

**Q1. Do control measures exist.**

If the answer is YES, then carry on to Q2.

If the answer if NO then by definition the step cannot be a CCP because it is not possible to effect control at this step. You must then ask the supplementary question "Is control at this step for safety?" If the answer is YES then it is necessary to modify that step or another step, or the process or product so that control is obtained over the specified hazard. The intention is that every hazard should be controlled at the CCP before the product leaves your hands, except those hazards that only your customer can control by their own handling practices. If the answer is NO then the step is not a CCP and the Decision Tree should be applied to the next identified hazard or step in the operation.

**Q2. Is the step specifically designed to eliminate or reduce the likely occurrence of a hazard to an acceptable level?**

If the answer is YES, then the step can be considered to be a CCP. This question allows flexibility, which would otherwise be denied by Q4. For example, steps such as evisceration or skinning in a slaughtering operation can be considered to be CCPs in addition to those that would be determined by consumer handling of the raw meat.

If the answer is NO, then carry on to Q3.

**Q3. Could contamination with identified hazards occur in excess of acceptable levels or could these increase to unacceptable levels?**

This question forces us to consider those steps that could permit the contamination or the growth of microorganisms such as storage or handling of the food between processing stages.

If the answer is NO, then the step cannot be a CCP because there is nothing that needs to be controlled. The whole decision tree is then repeated for the next hazard or step in the operation.

If the answer is YES, then carry on to Q4.

**Q4. Will a subsequent step eliminate identified hazards or reduce likely occurrence of the identified hazard to an acceptable level?**

If the answer is NO then the step is a CCP.

If the answer is YES then the step is not a CCP and the whole decision tree is repeated for the next hazard or step in the operation.

This question has a very important function to play when determining CCPs: it allows the presence of a hazard at a step if that hazard will subsequently, either as part of the operation or by some action of the end user, be eliminated or reduced to an acceptable likelihood of occurrence. Otherwise, every step in an operation might be critical leading to too many CCPs for an effective, practical control system to be drawn up.

Again, the keys to success with this question are flexibility and common sense. This question is designed to work in tandem with Q2. For example, the presence of low levels of salmonella in the raw meat ingredient for a ready to eat cooked meat prior to the cooking stage may be a concern but it might not necessarily be critical.

Another useful aspect of this question is that it focuses the thoughts of the HACCP team on the realistic end use of the product. For example, the importance and appropriateness of labelling instructions, say for cooking of a raw meat product such as a hamburger, become evident.

The authors gratefully acknowledge the contribution of Dr. Bob Mitchell who provided the discussion on the Codex Decision Tree.

## Appendix 4. HACCP and Assured Safe Catering

Catering in a large diverse industry ranging from small guest houses to large airline catering. Applying HACCP within catering brings additional problems including:

* Less technical expertise and facilities

* Wider product range

* Preparation and service

* Less formal quality assurance

* Higher staff turnover

* Less equipment and opportunities for monitoring

Whilst the HACCP approach has become a legal requirement for all food producers, the expectations for its implementation are not the same for all catering operations. HACCP principle have been adapted for use in catering in the development of Assured Safe Catering (ASC), or equivalent systems such as S.A.F.F. or S.C.A.P. It is likely that generic HACCP plans (covering a range of similar dishes - raw materials and processing) will be developed for many catering operations. An alternative approach to HACCP in food service in the USA is a process imitated approach.This approach decides on what operational steps are critical to a safe food outcome. Broadly speaking, 3 process types are:

Receive - Prepare - Serve

Receive - Prepare - Cook - Hold ? Serve

Receive - Prepare - Cook - Cool - Reheat - Hot Hold ? Serve

These basic process types can be seen in the flow diagrams on page 130

Within catering HACCP can be implemented at different levels. A basic level would suit small operations with limited resources and relatively little food handling. A more in-depth approach is required for larger establishments. The amount of detail required is likely to be proportional to the risk posed to the establishment.

## Basic flow diagram (Chicken Mayonaise Sandwich)

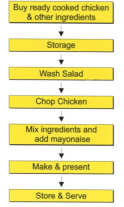

## Greater Depth Flow Diagram for chicken curry

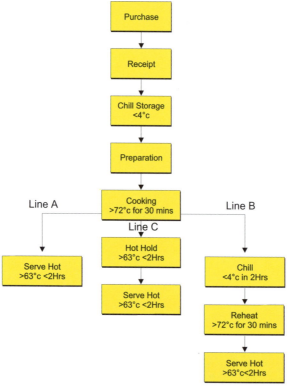

Pages 135-137 consider depth in relation to the construction of flow diagrams, identification of hazards and assessment of risk, risk management and communication within catering.

## Appendix 5

## 5. Risk Analysis, Risk Assessment, HACCP and PRP's

### 5.1. Background

Risk analysis and HACCP are closely linked and the precise interrelationship often causes confusion, nevertheless they are different with different outputs. Part of the problem is the term risk can be used in different ways, it is interpreted differently by people and translates differently between languages. In this book risk usually means the probability or likely occurrence of an event with or without consideration of hazard severity. It is possible to talk of the risk of food poisoning, risk of dying, high risk food, risk of contamination with a pathogen, food risk category, high risk consumer (here the term risk includes to severity as well as probability). Terms such as high risk, low risk are often indicating what is acceptable or unacceptable depending upon circumstances, context and country. Qualitative expressions of risk such as high, medium, low can be used alongside quantitative expressions such as 1:2.5 people carry Staphylococcus aureus in their nose or throat; 80% of poultry can be contaminated with campylobacter or 1:1500 catering premises are likely to give rise to food poisoning every year.

Attempts have been made to clarify the subject of Risk Analysis and provide a context for its use in food safety. The Codex Alimentarius Committee has drafted principles and guidelines for the application of Microbiological Risk Assessment and other books have also been written. One, Practical Microbiological Risk Analysis is of particular benefit to people working with HACCP and food safety. Risk analysis can have a highly structured meaning as expressed by Codex or can be used in a less clearly defined way in general discussion. Within the Codex approach, risk analysis is considered as having three component parts. One of the components of risk analysis is risk assessment which can be defined as "the scientific evaluation of known or potential adverse health effects resulting from human exposure to food borne hazards". More simply it is a process for identifying adverse consequences and their associated probability. Risk assessment can be quantitative or qualitative. Quantitative risk assessment whilst addressing uncertainties, emphasises reliance on numerical risk estimation. Currently within most HACCP plans qualitative risk assessment is used, although there have been calls / suggestions for the use of a more quantitative approach especially during the hazard analysis itself when the significance of each hazard is assessed. However for most companies, with the possible exception of multinational organisations, true quantitative risk assessment may be too complex. Whatever form of risk assessment is used it should guide the HACCP team in the construction of their plans. It should be noted that HACCP and PRPs are forms of risk management with PRPs, a general approach and HACCP specific for named hazards. In general terms PRPs do not themselves make use of risk data whilst HACCP does. The HACCP team needs to consider, especially during the hazard analysis, the risk data, qualitative or quantitative, e.g. in using decision trees. However, general hygiene or food safety training should be delivered in terms of hazard and risk (such as that offered by the RIPHH) so that food handlers are aware of the consequences of their activities and are prepared for working with HACCP.

A number of countries, especially the USA, have undertaken comprehensive and detailed "farm to fork" risk assessments and such documents can be useful to HACCP teams.

## 5.2. Risk Calculation or Estimation

Without engaging in a fully Quantitative Risk Assessment various forms of risk calculation or estimation can be useful to a HACCP team and guide expert judgement. These include:

• Calculation of the probability that a food product will be contaminated with a named pathogen, e.g. Salmonella contamination rates of poultry. Allocation of food to risk categories either based upon inherent properties of the food or the frequency of involvement in outbreaks of food poisoning.

- Assessment of epidemiological data to identify / rank risk factors, e.g. methods of preparation / food practices. This type of data is produced in a number of countries including USA, UK and Netherlands although it is often reported differently. Of interest is the continued rise of cross contamination as a risk factor. The latest UK data suggest cross contamination is a risk factor in 39% of general outbreaks of food poisoning but even this is likely to be a serious underestimate (due to how the data is collected). This emphasises the importance of control measures and cleaning post processing, e.g. after pasteurisation in the dairy industry, after cooking in food service.

- Risk of pathogen growth / survival, e.g. following or during processing.

Such risk estimates can be useful in a number of ways, including;

- Construction of a risk matrix for assessing the significance or ranking of hazards.

- As a prelude to the use of the Codex decision tree for determining critical points.

- To prioritise inspections.

- In risk based auditing.

- Demonstrating accuracy and transparency in decision making.

Data used in calculations can be obtained from many sources including epidemiological statistics, "in-house" microbiological testing, textbooks, predictive modelling, packages, journals, etc. Appendix 8 contains a detailed example of a simple risk profile adopted from Vosey, P, (2000).

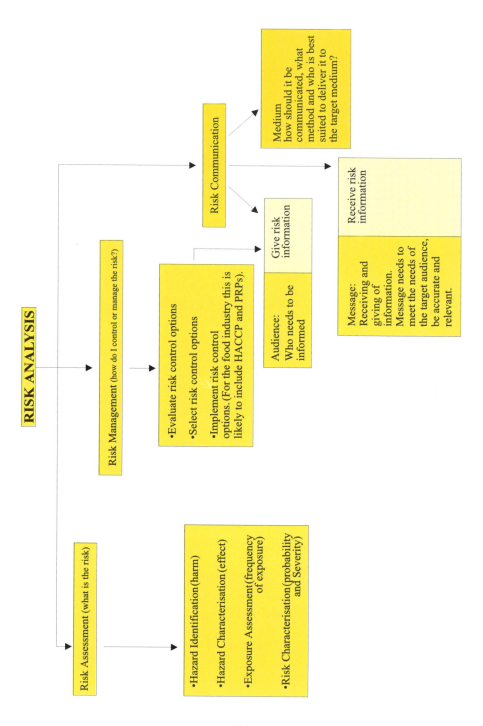

## 5.3 Examples of Expressions of risk at different levels

### 1. Probability of food poisoning from a catering operation in 1991.

**Basic Level -** Food Poisoning is a possibility.

| Greater Depth | Number of outbreaks of food poisoning associated with catering operations | Number of Catering Outlets | Risk |
|---|---|---|---|
| | 210 | 320,688 | 1 in 1527 |

### 2. Probability of Poultry Contamination with Salmonella.

**Basic Level -** Poultry is frequently contaminated with Salmonella.

| Greater Depth | Number of Chickens tested | Number positive for Salmonella | Risk |
|---|---|---|---|
| | 562 | 207 | 1 in 2.7 |

N.B. 700 milion chickens sold each year in the U.K.

### 3. Probability of Eggs contaminated with Salmonella.

**Basic Level -** Some eggs can be contaminated with Salmonella.

| Greater Depth | Number of Eggs tested | Number positive for Salmonella | Risk |
|---|---|---|---|
| | 7730 packs (6) | 17 | 1 in 455 |

N.B. 30 million eggs/day used in the U.K.

**4.     Probability of hands contaminated with Staphylococci.**

**Basic Level** - Hands may be contaminated with Staphylococci.

**Greater Depth** - 1 in 3 to 1 in 2 people have **Staphylococcus aureus on their hands.**

**Preventative Measures - Risk Management**

**1.     Prevention of Salmonellosis from Eggs.**

**Basic Level** - All eggs to be refrigerated in storage. All eggs well cooked. Clean and disinfect preparation areas thoroughly and wash hands after handling eggs.

**Greater Depth** - Description of detailed protocol for buying, storing and handling eggs to prevent growth, survival and cross contamination of Salmonella. Specific instructions given on individual dishes e.g. use of raw eggs in making Tiramisu.

**2.     Prevention of Salmonellosis from Poultry.**

**Basic Level** - All poultry to be stored refrigerated or frozen. Frozen poultry to be defrosted thoroughly. Cook thoroughly according to instructions, clean and disinfect preparation areas in contact with raw poultry.

**Greater Depth** - Detailed procedures for buying, storing and handling of poultry to prevent growth, survival and cross contamination of Salmonella. Specific instructions given on how defrosting and cooling to be performed, plus detailed monitoring instructions to assess if control measures implemented.

**Risk Communication**

**Storage of Egg sandwiches**

**Basic Level** - Verbal or minimal written instructions about handling eggs given to staff and/or Environmental Health Officers.

**Greater Depth** - Detailed documentation containing instructions in food handling/ preparation/ storage practices. Documentation containing full and detailed monitoring procedures and records.

Evidence of tests on refrigeration efficiency. For use in staff training or for EHO and if required, due diligence defence.

**Worked Example (In Depth) of an Assured Safe Catering Worksheet for Cooked Chicken**

**Step** - Number 6 Cooking (i.e. 6th step in the flow diagram)

**Hazard & Risk** - Foodborne pathogens high risk of Salmonella and Campylobacter. Other possible pathogens Clostridium perfringens, Listeria monocytogenes.

**Source** - Poultry carcass

**Worked Example (In Depth) of an ASC Worksheet for Cooked Chicken**

**Preventative Measures** - Product reached a sufficiently high temperature to kill vegetative pathogens.

This depends upon; Size of bird, initial temperature of bird, oven temperature, oven efficiency, cooking time, end point centre temperature.

**CCP** - Use of the Simple Logic Tree (page 50) indicates this is a CCP.

**Worked Example (In Depth) of an ASC Worksheet for Cooked Chicken**

| Target Values and Critical Limits: | Bird size | 3kg ± 0.25kg |
| --- | --- | --- |
| | Initial temp | 8°C ± 2°C |
| | Oven temp | 170°C ± 1°C |
| | Oven efficiency | ± 5°C of setting |
| | Cooking time | 155 mins ± 2.5 mins |
| | End temp | 82°C ± 2°C |

| Monitoring How: | Weigh 1 in 10 birds |
| --- | --- |
| | Check, probe thermometer (1 in 4) |
| | Check, oven setting |
| | Oven efficiency check |
| | Check, start and finish time |
| | Check, probe thermometer (1 in 10) |

| Monitoring: | When | Who |
| --- | --- | --- |
| | Time of delivery | Purchasing Officer |
| | Prior to cooking | Chef |
| | Start of cooking | Chef |
| | Every 3 months | Head Chef |
| | At start and finish | Chef |
| | At end of cooking time | Chef |

## Appendix 6 : Possible CCPs and Common Critical Limits
### Table 13
### Examples of possible Critical Control Points

| Raw Products | Heat Processed/Cooked Products |
|---|---|
| Product raw materials. | Product raw materials. |
| Chilling raw materials. | Heat processing of raw materials. |
| Chilled storage and distridution. | Chilling cooked product. |
| | Product assembly/portioning. |
| | Chilled storage/distribution. |

### Table 14
### Examples of Target Values and Critical Limits.

| Hazard | Control Measure | Target Value value | Critical Limits |
|---|---|---|---|
| Microbiological growth in raw meat | Temperature Control | Frozen -18°C Chilled meat +3°C | -17--20°C +1-+4°C |
| Microbiological survival in product | Correct cooking* time and temp. | Heat processing must ensure a minimum centre temp. of +75°C | +74-+76°C (this incorporates a safety margin for the most resistant vegative pathogen present) |
| Microbiological growth if temperature abuse | Correct holding temperature | Centre Temperature to be at +75°C | +62-+72°C |
| Cross contamination of work surface in contact with heat processed product | Effective cleaning procedures | 100 RLUs** | 250 RLUs |
| Metal pieces in product | Metal detector | Absence | Min. ferrous 2.0mg Non-ferrous 2.5ng |
| Microbiological growth | Correct holding temperature | +3°C | +2-+4°C |
| Presence of Aflatoxin | Certified raw materials | Absence | <10mg/Kg |

**Notes:**

These are examples of typical critical limits which may be used. Actual values will depend upon the product being produced and identified hazards.

\* A correct heat processing should specify the temperature and time for heat processing and a minimum centre temperature. In order to achieve these other preventative measures may need to be used eg. for meat specify the size/weight of the product, initial temperature etc. These are all factors which can determine terminal centre temperature.

\*\* RLUs are relative light units and are obtained by means of a luminometer. Actual values will vary depending upon the background reading, make of instrument and the typical variation encountered after thorough cleaning. If felt necessary traditional microbiological techniques, swabs and contact plates can be used as a backup. This could confirm the relationship between viable microbial numbers and food ATP for the type of product surface and give an indication of the type of organism present.

## Appendix 7: Validation and Verification

Considerable debate concerns the use of the terms validation and verification, in this book the authors have followed the philosophy outlined by ILSI.

Validation concerns obtaining evidence that the elements of the HACCP plan are effective. This is particularly important during the behavioural evaluation phase of the hazard analysis as well as during the implementation phase to ensure the plan as a whole is effective. Validation should ensure that the information supporting the HACCP plan is correct and can be useful in the design stage and taken on as new scientific information becomes available.

Verification is the application of methods, procedures, tests and other evaluations in addition to monitoring to determine compliance with the HACCP plan. Thus, once the HACCP plan has been designed and validated (i.e. it is capable of consistently delivering safe food), it is important that it is being adhered to or complied with, i.e. are you doing what you claim you are doing.

**Examples of Validation and Conformity Verification (ILSI 1999)**

| HACCP Principles | Validation. Evidence to Demonstrate That: | Verification: Evidence to Demonstrate That: |
|---|---|---|
| 1. Hazard Analysis | The correct skills were in the HACCP team.<br><br>The flow diagrams suitable for the purposes of the HACCP study and all the significant hazards were identified | Validation was carried out correctly |
| 2. Determination of the CCPs required to control identified hazards | All significant hazards were considered during CCP identification.<br>There are CCPs to control all significant hazards.<br>The CCPs are at the appropriate stages in the process | Validation was carried out correctly |
| 3. Specification of critical limits to assure that an operation is under control at a particular CCP | The critical limits control the identified hazards | Validation was carried out correctly |
| 4. Establishment and implementation of systems to monitor control of CCPs | The monitoring system will ensure that the control measures at the CCPs will be effective.<br><br>Procedures for the necessary calibration of testing equipment are included | Records for monitoring exist and confirm control.<br>Statistical process control is used.<br>Designated person's review of record monitoring.<br>Records of calibration exist and confirm compliance |
| 5. Establishment of the corrective action to be taken when monitoring indicates that a particular CCP is not under control | Corrective action plans will prevent non-conforming product from reaching the consumer.<br>Authority for corrective actions has been assigned. | In cases of non-conformity, control is regained.<br><br>Corrective actions are recorded and actions taken by designated persons. |
| 6. Establishment of procedures for verification to confirm that the HACCP system is working effectively | Procedures for information gathering and compliance verification of the HACCP system have been established | All verification procedures are carried out |
| 7. Establishment of documentation concerning all procedures and records appropriate to these principles and their application | Documentation covering the entire HACCP system has been established | Documentation and record keeping covering the entire HACCP system is complete, in the correct format, and properly filled out. |

## Recommended Company HACCP Verification Schedule (NACMSF (USA))

| ACTIVITY | FREQUENCY | RESPONSIBILITY | REVIEWER |
|---|---|---|---|
| Verification Activities Schedule | Yearly or upon HACCP system change | HACCP Co-ordinator | Plant Manager |
| Initial Validation of HACCP Plan | Prior to and during initial implementation of plan | Independent experts(s)1 | HACCP Team |
| Subsuquent Validation of HACCP Plan | When critical limits changed, significant changes in process, equipment changed, after system failure, etc... | Independent experts(s)1 | HACCP Team |
| Verification of CCP Monitoring as Described in the Plan (e.g. monitoring of patty cooking temperature) | According to HACCP plan (e.g. once per shift) | According to HACCP plan (e.g. Line Supervisor) | According to HACCP plan (e.g. Quality control) |
| Review of Monitoring, Corrective Action Records to show Compliance with the plan | Monthly | Quality Assurance | HACCP Team |
| Comprehensive HACCP System Verification | Plant Manager | Independent experts(s)1 | |

1 Performed by other than the teams writing and implementing the plan. May require additional technical expertise as well as laboratory and plant test studies.

# Appendix 8: Microbiological Risk assessment

## Risk profile example/Staphylococcus aureus and Listeria monocytogenes in cooked ham

| | | |
|---|---|---|
| Warning - these are examples only | | |
| Ratings (1-5) are given in bold, those associated with quality of information (uncertainty) are in shaded boxes and are added separately at the end to give the 'information quality profile' | | |

| Question | Risk assessment 1 | Risk assessment 2 |
|---|---|---|
| **Hazard Identification** | | |
| *1. What is the name and type of product?* | Cooked ham | Cooked ham |
| *2. What are the micro-organisms realistically associated with the product?* | *Listeria monocytogenes, Staphylococcus aureus, Salmonella* Typhimurium | *Listeria monocytogenes, Staphylococcus aureus, Salmonella* Typhimurium |
| *2.1 What is the micro-organism covered by this risk assessment?* | *Staphylococcus aureus* | *Listeria monocytogenes* |
| *2.2 Is it toxigenic or not ?* | Yes | No |
| **Hazard Characterisation** | | |
| *3.1 Who are the consumers of concern ?* | Families | Families |
| *3.2 How many distinctive sub-groups are there in the population of consumers?* | Children, adults, the old. | Pregnant women, immuno-compromised |
| *3.3 What is the severity of the hazard (the sensitivity of each group should be considered or that of the most sensitive consumers should be used for a single assessment)?* | **3** Generally, mild symptoms but some case of hospitalisation | **4** Severe symptoms, hospitalisation some deaths |
| *3.4 What is the hazardous level of the micro-organism covered by this risk assessment?* | **1** more than $10^4$ cells | **4** Low minimum dose : 10-100 cells |
| *3.5 What is the uncertainty of this estimate?* | **3** Quantitative general - information on similar microbe and food | **1** Accurate, precise data on relevant microbe and food |
| **Exposure assessment (occurrence of the hazardous micro-organism)** | | |
| *4.1 What is the frequency of contamination of the raw materials making up the product?* | **3** Low frequency : 1/100 | **5** Always |
| *4.2 What is the range of levels of contamination found in the raw materials?* | **3** $0-10^3$ cells/g | **4** $0-10^4$ cells/g |
| *4.3 How uncertain is this estimate?* | **4** Qualitative general information on similar microbe and food | **4** Qualitative general information on similar microbe and food |

| Question | Risk assessment 1 | Risk assessment 2 |
|---|---|---|
| **Exposure assessment - Effect of processing/decontamination** | | |
| 5.1  *What is the effect of storage before processing on the level of the hazard?* | 3  0-$10^3$ cells/g | 5  more than $10^4$ cells/g |
| 5.2  *What is the intended effect of all processing and any decontamination stages on the level of the micro-organism?* | 1  Inactivation: At least 6-log decrease in numbers for both microorganisms | 1  Inactivation: At least 6-log decrease in numbers for both microorganisms |
| 5.3  *What is the uncertainty of this estimate?* | 1  Accurate, precise data on similar microbe and food | 1  Accurate, precise data on similar microbe and food |
| **Exposure assessment - Occurrence of toxin (if the hazardous micro-organism is toxigenic)** | | |
| 6.1  *What is the likelihood of toxin presence if the micro-organism contaminates the raw materials or product?* | 3  Low frequency : 1/100 | N/a |
| 6.2  *What is the uncertainty of this estimate?* | 5  Opinion / default, no hard data | N/a |
| **Exposure assessment - Re-contamination after processing or decontamination** | | |
| 7.1  *What is the frequency of re-contamination of the product in the factory after processing or decontamination, so that the hazard is present in the final product?* | 2  Very low frequency : 1/1000 | 2  Very low frequency : 1/1000 |
| 7.2  *What is the likely level of re-contamination after processing or decontamination?* | 2  0-$10^2$ cells/g | 1  0-10 cells/g |
| 7.3  *What is the uncertainty of this estimate?* | 1  Accurate precise data on similar microbe and food | 1  Accurate precise data on similar microbe and food |
| **Exposure assessment - Packaging** | | |
| 8.1  *Is the product put in its primary packaging before (**yes**) or after (**no**) the decontamination step ?* | No (after) | No (after) |
| 8.2  *If the answer to 8.1 is **yes**- what is the effectiveness of packaging at preventing recontamination before consumption?* | N/a | N/a |
| 8.3  *What is the frequency of recontamination after packaging?* | 1  Never | 1  Never |

| Question | Risk assessment 1 | Risk assessment 2 |
|---|---|---|
| 8.4 *What is the level of recontamination after packaging?* | **1** 0 - 10 cells/g | **1** 0 - 10 cells/g |
| 8.5 *What is the uncertainty of the estimate?* | **1** Accurate precise data on similar microbe and food | **1** Accurate precise data on similar microbe and food |

## Exposure assessment - Effect of product storage

| | | |
|---|---|---|
| 9.1 *How does the level of the microorganism change during product storage?* | **3** No change: survival. | **4** Slow growth : less than 3 log increase in numbers |
| 9.2 *What is the uncertainty of this estimate?* | **3** Quantitative general information on similar microbe and food | **3** Quantitative general information on similar microbe and food |
| 9.3 *What is the effect of storage of the final product (according to the usage instructions) on the level of toxin?* | **3** No change : survival | **4** Slow growth : less than 3 log increase in numbers |
| 9.4 *What is the effect of storage conditions on toxigenesis (If the level of the micro-organism changes and it is toxigenic)* | **3** No change : survival - no toxin production | N/a |
| 9.5 *What is the likelihood of toxigenesis in the product?* | **3** Possible | N/a |
| 9.6 *What is the uncertainty of this estimate?* | **4** Qualitative general information on similar microbe and food | **4** Qualitative general information on similar microbe and food |

## Exposure assessment - Consumer use

| | | |
|---|---|---|
| 10.1 *Is the product intended as single use (**yes**) or multi-use (**no**), with storage after opening?* | No | No |
| 10.2 **If the answer to 10.1. is No, this means that the product is multi-use either in a domestic or food service application, and sections 11 & 12 must be completed.** | | |

## Exposure assessment - The effect of open shelf-life on the microbial hazard

| | | |
|---|---|---|
| 11.1 *What is the effect of open shelf-life storage on the level of micro-organisms ?* | **3** No change - survival | **4** Slow growth : Less than 3-log increase in numbers |
| 11.2 *What is the uncertainty of this estimate?* | **5** Opinion / default, no hard data | **1** Accurate precise data on similar microbe and food |

| Question | Risk assessment 1 | Risk assessment 2 |
|---|---|---|
| **Exposure assessment - The effect of open shelf-life on toxigenesis** | | |
| 12.1 *What is the likelihood of growth and toxin production during open shelf-life?* | 4 Slow growth: Less than 3-log increase in numbers - low chance of toxin production | N/a |
| 12.2 What is the uncertainty of this estimate? | 4 Qualitative general information on similar microbe and food | N/a |
| **Exposure assessment - The effect of usage and preparation on the level of the hazardous micro-organisms** | | |
| 13.1 *What is the effect of customer or food service preparation and usage on the level of hazard?* | 3 No changes : survival. | 4 Slow growth : Less than 3-log increase in numbers |
| 13.2 *What is the uncertainty of this estimate?* | 5 Opinion / default, no hard data | 5 Opinion / default, no hard data |
| 13.3 *What is the effect of usage and preparation on toxin level and production?* | 3 Unchanged | N/a |
| 13.4 *What is the probability of toxin presence at the point of consumption?* | 2 Very low frequency : 1/1000 | N/a |
| 13.5 *What is the uncertainty of this estimate?* | 5 Opinion, no hard data | N/a |
| **Exposure assessment - Food intake by a consumer** | | |
| 14.1 *What is the likely quantity of the food consumed by a customer on a specified occasion or over a period of time?* | 3 Medium intake : 50-100g | 3 Medium intake : 50-100g |
| 14.2 *What is the uncertainty of this estimate?* | 3 Quantitative general information on similar microbe and food | 3 Quantitative general information on similar microbe and food |
| **Risk profile - total 'score'** **Risk profile - comparable 'score'-** excluding toxin specific scores | 53 35 **Excluding score from** 6.1, 9.4, 9.5, 12.1, 13.3, 13.4 | 47 47 |
| **Information quality profile** | 44 | 24 |

**Risk Profile Example with permission from CCFRAG (2000) An introduction to the practice of microbiological risk assessment for food industry applications. CCFRA Guideline 28. ISBN 0 905942 33 7**

## Appendix 9 : Guidelines for the application of the HACCP systems for small less developed businesses (SLDB's)

### Proposed revised Guidelines to be discussed in Codex Committee on Food Hygiene, Washington, 23-28 October 2000

The prerequisites to HACCP, including training, should be well established, fully operational and verified in order to facilitate the successful application and implementation of the HACCP system. For all types of food business management commitment is necessary for implementation of an effective HACCP system.

It is important when applying HACCP to be flexible where appropriate, given the context of the application, taking into account the nature and size of the operation, including available resources, processes, techniques and practical constraints. This may be particularly relevant in small less developed businesses. All seven principles must be applied in the HACCP system.

### APPLICATION

### 1. Assemble HACCP team

Where such expertise is not available on site, expert advice should be obtained from other sources, such as regulatory authorities, trade and industry associations, independent experts and HACCP literature and guidance (including sector-specific guides)

Expertly developed HACCP guidance relevant to the process or type of operation may provide a useful tool for businesses in their application of HACCP principles. It may be possible that a well-trained individual in possession of such guidance documents is able to implement HACCP in-house.

### 2. Describe product

In multi-product businesses, such as for example, catering operations, it may be effective to focus on groups of products with similar characteristics or processing steps that are used for a number of similar products.

## 3. Identify intended use

Where businesses are using expertly developed HACCP guidance, it is important that this is specific to the foods and/or processes under consideration.

## 4. Construct flow diagram

The flow diagram should cover all steps in the operation for a particular product. When similar processing steps are used for a number of products the same flow diagram may be used.

## 5. On-site confirmation of flow diagram

Steps must be taken to confirm the processing operation against the flow diagram during all stages and hours of operation and amend the flow diagram where appropriate. The confirmation of the flow diagram should be performed by a person with sufficient knowledge of the processing operation.

## 6. Identify and list all relevant hazards and control measures

List all potential hazards associated with each step, conduct a hazard analysis and consider any measures to control identified hazards.
(SEE PRINCIPLE 1)

The HACCP team (see also paragraph 1 above) should list all of the hazards that may be reasonably expected to occur at each step from primary production, processing manufacture, and distribution until the point of consumption

The HACCP team (see also paragraph 1 above) should next conduct a hazard analysis to identify for the HACCP plan, which hazards are of such a nature that their elimination or reduction to acceptable levels is essential to the production of a safe food.

Considerations should be given to what control measures, if any exist, can be applied to each hazard.

To facilitate the hazard analysis, businesses may consult sources of expert information on identifying hazards relevant to the process and the control measures necessary. This information, such as expertly developed guideline documents, should be considered as reference material to the identification of the specific hazards and controls within the operation.

**7. Determine Critical Control Points** (SEE PRINCIPLE 2)
To facilitate the CCP determination, businesses may consult sources of expert information on identifying CCPs relevant to the product/process. This information, such as expertly developed guideline documents, should be considered as reference material to the identification of CCPs.

**8. Establish critical limits for each CCP** (SEE PRINCIPLE 3)
Critical limits must be specified and validated for each Critical Control Point.

Expertly developed HACCP guidance can help businesses, in particular *SLDBs, in identifying the most appropriate criteria for the critical limits as well as the limits themselves. Care should be taken to ensure that these limits fully apply to the specific operation or product under consideration. These critical limits should be measurable.

**9. Establish a monitoring system for each CCP**
(SEE PRINCIPLE 4)
The efficacy of any monitoring system will rely on management and employees having the appropriate knowledge and skills especially where monitoring arrangements are carried out manually.

**10.     Establish correction actions** (SEE PRINCIPLE 5)
Where in-house expertise is not available, external expertise may be needed to advise on the appropriate corrective actions to be taken when there is a loss of control.

**11.     Establish verification procedures** (SEE PRINCIPLE 6)
Verification should be carried out by someone other than the person

who is responsible for performing the monitoring and corrective actions. Where verification can not be performed in house, verification may be performed on behalf of the company by external experts.

The ability to perform validation will vary depending upon the nature and size of the business and the availability of resources.

Expertly developed HACCP guidance can help businesses, particularly *SLDBs in identifying the most appropriate criteria for verification and validation activities. Care should be taken to ensure that these activities apply to the specific operation or product under consideration in a suitable way.

## 12. Establish Documentation and Record Keeping
### (SEE PRINCIPLE 7)
Documentation and record keeping should be appropriate to the nature and size of the operation and sufficient to enable the business to be confident that controls are in place and being maintained.

Record examples are:

• Verification procedures performed;
• Modifications to the HACCP plan;

A simple record-keeping system can be effective and easily communicated to employees. It may be integrated into existing operations and may use existing paperwork, such as delivery invoices and checklists to record, for example, product temperatures.

* SLDB's – Small and less developed business

**Appendix 10**      **USEFUL REFERENCES:**

Bell, C, Kyriakides (1998), A. E.coli A practical approach to the organism and its control in foods, London, Blackie Academic & Professional.

Bell, C, Kyriakides (1998), A. Listeria A practical approach to the organism and its control in foods, London, Blackie Academic & Professional.

Bicheno, J. (1992). 34 for Quality. PICSIE Books. Buckingham. MK 18 7YE

Blanchfield, J.R. (1992). Due diligence- Defence or system. Food Control (3).

Bryan, F. (1992). W.H.O. Hazard Analysis Critical Control Point Evaluations. Geneva

B.S.I. Quality Systems for the Food and Drink Industries. Guide-lines for the use of BS 5750 part 2. 1987(Leatherhead Food Research Association) 1989 and revised November 1991.

Leaper, S. (1997) HACCP: a practical Guide. Second Edition. CCFRA Technical Manual No. 38 Campden & Chorleywood Food research Association. Chipping Campden, Gloucester.

CCFRAG (2000) An Introduction to the practice of microbiological risk assessment for food industry applications. CCFRA Guideline 28. ISBN 0 905942 33 7

Codex Alimentarius-1997. Guidelines for the Application of the Hazard Analysis Critical Control Point System- ALINORM 97/13A. Appendix II

Cortlett, D.A. Jnr (1998) HACCP Users Manual. Cortlett Food Consulting Service, Concord California. Aspen Publisher Inc, Maryland, USA.

Dillon, M. (1992). Confrontation or collaboration. Appropriate Technology.(19) No 1.

Dillon, M and Ogier, J. (1992). The Development of appropriate quality management systems in Europe. Proceedings of the International Horticulture Economics Conference,Montpellier. July

Dillon, M, Horner, W.F.A., Ogier, J.P.O. and Quantick, P. (1995). Chemical and Physical Hazards, A case study. Flair-Flow Europe, June 19th, Cardiff.

Flair-Flow Europe, Conference papers June 95, HACCP Knowing Your Enemies and Your Friends. Published by M.D. Associates.

Food Control, Special issue on HACCP (1994). Basic principles, applications and training. Volume No. 5

Food Safety Act 1990. Code of Practice 8 . Food Standards Inspection. HMSO 1991

Food Safety Act. Code of Practice 9. Food Hygiene Inspection. HMSO 1991, revised 1999

Griffith, C.J., Mortlock, M.P., Peters, A.C., 'Evaluating the Economic Impact of HACCP Implemetation in Welsh Butchers Shops.' Second NSF International Conference on Food Safety, Savannah, Georgia, USA, 2000

Gombas D.E. and Stevenson K.R. (2000) HACCP Verification and Validation: An Advanced HACCP Workshop, 2nd Edition. Food Processors Institute, Washimgton, USA.

HACCP User Guide. (1994). Food Linked Agro Industrial Research.

Harrigan, W.F and Park, R.W.A. (1991). Making Safe Food. Academic Press. London.

Horner, W.F.A. and Dillon, M. (1994). Evaluation of a practically based approach to the implementation of HACCP systems in the manufacture of seafood products. International Seafood Conference, WEFTA.

Horner, W.F.A. and Dillon, M. (1995). HACCP - the commonsense approach to fish product safety. Seafood International.

Hudak -Roos, M. and Spencer Garrett, E. (1992). Monitoring, corrective actions and record keeping in HACCP .In Quality Assurance in the Fish Industry. Edited by H.H Huss et al. Published by Elsevier

Huss, H.H. (1994) Assurance of Seafood Quality, FAO Fisheries Technical Paper, 334, Rome

ICMSF (1996) Microorganisms in Food 5. Microbial Ecology of Food Commodities. Blackie Academic and Professional. London

ICMSF (1998) Microorganisms in Food 6. Microbial Ecology of Food Commodities. Blackie Academic and Professional. London

Institute of Food Science and Technology (1991) . Food And Drink. Good Manufacturing Practice. 3rd Edition. Edited by K.G.Anderson and J.R.Blanchfield.

Institute of Food Science and Technology (1993). List of codes of Practice applicable to Food.

International Life Science Institute (1999) Validation and Verification of HACCP. A report prepared by the ILSI Europe Risk Analysis in Microbiology Task Force. Brussels. ILSI Europe.

Jansen, J.T., ' (2000) Application of HACCP Principles in Small and Less Developed Businesses (SLBDS) With a Focus on Recent Discussions in Codex Alimentarius and During WHO Expert Consultations. 2nd NSF International Conference on Food Safety, Savannah Georgia, USA.

Mitchell, R.T. (2000)Practical Microbiological Risk Analysis. How to assess, manage and communicate microbiological risks in food, Chandos Publishing Ltd, Oxford

Mortimore, S and Wallace, C (1998) HACCP - A practical approach, 2nd Edition. Aspen Publications Inc, Maryland, USA.

NACMF: National Advisory Committee on Microbiological Criteria for foods (1992) HACCP system. International Journal of food Microbiology Volume 16.

Notermans, S., Mead, G.C. and Jouve, J.L. (1996) Food Products and consumer protection : A conceptive approach and a glossary of terms. International Journal of Food Microbiology, 30, 175 - 183

Panisello, P.J., and Quantick P.C. (2000) HACCP and its instruments: A managers guide. Chandos Publishing (Oxford) Ltd. Oxford.

Pearson A.M. and Dutson T.R. (1995) HACCP in Meat, Poultry and Fish Processing: Advances in meat research series, Volume 10. Blackie Academic and Professional, Glasgow

Pierson, M.D. and Corlett, D.A. (1992). HACCP Principles and applications. Chapman and Hall. London.

Report of the FAO Expert Technical Meeting on the Use of HACCP Principles in Food Control (1994), 12-16 December. Vancouver

Royal Institute of Public Health and Hygiene. (1995). HACCP Principles and their Applications in Food Safety (Introductory course). Training Standard. R.I.P.H.H. 28 Portland Place, London WIN 4DE.

Shapton, D.A. and Shapton, N. (1993). Principles and practices for the safe processing of food. Butterworth Heinemann

Spencer-Garrett, E. 'Along the Yellow Brick Road Toward Microbiological Risk assessment'. The Canadian Food Inspection Agency's Anual Conference, Vancouver, 2000.

Spencer-Garrett, E. III and Martha Hudak-Roos.(1991). Developing a HACCP based inspection system for the Seafood industry. Food Technology, December.

Stevenson K.E. and Bernard D.T. (1999) HACCP A Systematic Approach to Food Safety, 3rd Edition. The Food Processors Institute, Washington, USA.

Tromans, S.(1993). Food Manufacturers and the Application of Hazard Analysis Critical Control Point. M.Sc. Thesis . University of Humberside.

Vosey, P. (2000) An Introduction to the Practice of Microbiological Risk Assessment for Food Industry Applications. TableA2.4 Example 1 - Risk Profile Example of Staph. aureus and Listeria monoctygenes in cooked ham, Campden and Chorleywood Food Research Assosciation Group, Chipping Campden.

WHO (1999). Strategies for Implementing HACCP in small businesses. Report of WHO Consulation in collaboration with the Ministry of Health, Welfare and Sports. The Hague, Netherlands. June

**List of useful websites:**

European Chilled Food Federation
http://www.chilledfood.org/ecff.htm

Institute of Food Research http://www.ifrn.bbsrc.ac.uk

Chartered Inststitute of Environmental Health http://www.cieh.org.uk

Codex Alimentarius Commision

http://www.fao.org/waicent/faoinfo/economic/esn/codex/Default.htm

Food Standards Agency http://www.foodstandards-gov.uk

European Union http://www.europa.eu.int/

LACOTS http://www.lacots.com

MAFF Food Safety http://www.maff.gov.uk/foodrin/fdindx.htm

US Govt Food Safety Information http://www.foodsafety.gov/